FOUNDATION
SCIENCE to 14

Stephen Pople

OXFORD
UNIVERSITY PRESS

Great Clarendon Street, Oxford OX2 6DP

Oxford University Press is a department of the University of Oxford.
It furthers the University's objective of excellence in research, scholarship,
and education by publishing worldwide in

Oxford New York

Athens Auckland Bangkok Bogotá Buenos Aires Calcutta
Cape Town Chennai Dar es Salaam Delhi Florence Hong Kong Istanbul
Karachi Kuala Lumpur Madrid Melbourne Mexico City Mumbai
Nairobi Paris São Paulo Singapore Taipei Tokyo Toronto Warsaw
with associated companies in Berlin Ibadan

Oxford is a registered trade mark of Oxford University Press
in the UK and in certain other countries

British Library Cataloguing in Publication Data

Data available

ISBN 0 19 914784 1

Typeset in Folio light/medium
Printed in Spain by Gráficas Estella, S. A.

Acknowledgements

The publisher would like to thank the following for their kind permission to reproduce photographs:

Allsport /Didier Klein p 85, p 89, /David Cannon p 90, /Bob Martin p 92; Bruce Coleman
/Dr Frieder Sauer p 11, /David Davies p 15, p 38, /Kim Taylor p 42, /Gerald Cubitt p 44 (Bottom
right), /Kim Taylor p 44 (bottom left), /Gordon Langsbury p 44 (top left), /Frank Greenaway p 45
(top right), /Kim Taylor p 45 (top left), p 46, /John Murray p 66 (Bottom right), /Dieter & Mary
Plage p 68, /George McCarthy p 71, /Mr Jens Rydell p 74 (bottom right); J Allen Cash p 24,
p 38 (bottom), p 43, p 53, p 56, p 96; GSF Picture Library p 74 (centre right and centre left),
/Dr B Booth p 75 (top left and top right); Oxford Scientific Films p 66 (bottom left), /Doug Allen
p 74 (bottom left), /Edward Parker p 94 (top left), p108; Science Photo Library /C Nuridsany &
M Perrennou p 11, /David Scharf p 28, /Petit Format/Nestle p 30 (top left, top middle, and top
right), /Katrina Thomas p 31, /Dr Tony Brain p 34, /Alex Bartel p 62 (bottom right), /European
Space Agency p 70, /Gordon Garradd p 76, /Takeshi Takahara p 91, /Photo Library International
p 94 (top right), /Johnny Autrey p 103, p 110, /NASA p 116 (bottom left), p 117, /David Parker p
116 (bottom right), /National Snow and Ice Data Services p 116 (top right); Tony StoneWorldwide
/Tom Tietz p 38 (top), p 64; Tony Waltham p 74 (top right).

Cover photo: **GettyOne Stone/Tim Flach**.

Additional photography by **Peter Gould**, **Martin Sookias** and **Chris Honeywell**.

The illustrations are by:

Chris Duggan, **Jeff Edwards**, **Jones Sewell**, **Pat Murray**, **Mike Nicholson**, **Mike Ogden**,
Oxford Illustrators, **Pat Thorne**, **Borin Van Loon**, and **Pamela Venus**.

Test and check

Can you answer these questions? If not, the spread number tells you where to find out more.

1 What are cells?
2 How are animal cells different from plant cells?
3 What is tissue?

2.01

4 Where is food made in a plant?
5 How does a plant get the energy to make its food?
6 What gas is made when an animal 'burns up' its food?

2.02

7 In a flower, where are the male cells and where are the female cells?
8 What does 'pollination' mean?
9 Why do some flowers have bright colours?

2.03

10 What happens at fertilization?
11 What is a fruit?
12 How are seeds produced?
13 What happens to seeds?

2.04

14 In your body, how do food, water, and oxygen get to your cells?
15 What job is done by the heart?
16 What job is done by the kidneys?

2.05

17 Why do you need a skeleton?
18 What job is done by the skull?
19 What is the main mineral in bone?
20 What moves your joints?

2.06

21 What are the main parts of the gut?
22 What happens to food in digestion?
23 What are enzymes?
24 What happens to food when it has been digested?

2.07

25 Why does your body need oxygen?
26 What carries food and oxygen to cells?
27 What 'exhaust gases' do you breathe out as a result of respiration?
28 What are capillaries?

2.08

29 What job is done by the lungs?
30 How does oxygen get into blood?
31 Which way does your diaphragm move when you breathe in?

2.09

32 In a woman, what do the ovaries do?
33 What happens to an egg during fertilization?
34 In a man, where are sperms stored?

2.10

35 In humans, how many months are there between fertilization and birth?
36 Before a baby is born, how does it get its food and oxygen?

2.11

37 Why do you need to eat proteins?
38 What foods are rich in vitamin C?
39 What substances give you most of your energy?

2.12

40 What are germs?
41 How can germs spread from one person to another?
42 What do antibiotics do?

2.13

43 What problems can you have if your diet is poor?
44 Why is smoking harmful?
45 Why is sniffing solvents dangerous?

2.14

46 Can you give some human features which show variation?
47 Can you give an example of selective breeding?

2.15

48 What are 'vertebrates'?
49 What are the five main groups of vertebrates?
50 What group do humans belong to?

2.16

51 What is a 'habitat'?
52 How do humans change the habitats of animals and plants?
53 What is sustainable development?

2.17

54 Can you describe how one animal is adapted to its way of life?
55 Why do many trees lose their leaves in the autumn?

2.18

56 Can you give an example of a food chain?
57 What is a 'predator'?
58 What is a 'prey'?

2.19

Test and check

Can you answer these questions? If not, the spread number tells you where to find out more.

1 How many grams are there in a kilogram?
2 What is a measuring cylinder used for?
3 Water has a 'density of 1000 kg/m^3'. Can you explain what this means?
4 How is a liquid different from a solid?
5 How is a gas different from a liquid?

3.01

6 What does a liquid become when it evaporates?
7 What is the temperature of boiling water?
8 What is the temperature of freezing water?

3.02

9 Can you describe how the particles behave in a solid and in a liquid?
10 Can you describe how the particles behave in a gas?
11 Can you explain what causes gas pressure?

3.03

12 About how many elements are there?
13 What are the two main types of element?
14 What is the smallest bit of an element called?
15 What is a compound?

3.04

16 What is meant by a 'pure' substance?
17 What is an alloy? Can you give an example of an alloy?
18 What do 'solute', 'solvent', and 'solution' mean?

3.05

19 How would you separate sand from water?
20 How would you separate salt from water?
21 How would you separate inks in a mixture?

3.06

22 If an acid is 'dilute', what does this mean?
23 What effect does an alkali have on an acid?
24 How does an acid affect litmus paper?
25 How does an alkali affect litmus paper?

3.07

26 Can you give an example of a chemical change?
27 What are the signs of a chemical change?
28 Can you give an example of a physical change?

3.08

29 What do you see if a substance reacts rapidly with oxygen?
30 Can you describe a simple test for oxygen?
31 What three things are needed for burning?

3.09

32 What two things are needed for iron to go rusty?
33 Gold is 'unreactive'. What does this mean?
34 What gas is produced when a metal reacts with an acid?

3.10

35 What are the two main gases in air? Which of these gases is there most of? Which of these gases do animals and plants need to stay alive?
36 Can you name one other gas in air? Can you describe any uses of this gas?

3.11

37 What is a saturated solution?
38 If a substance dissolves in water, how does temperature affect the amount which will dissolve?
39 What damage can water cause when it freezes?

3.12

40 What happens to a rock during 'weathering'?
41 Can you give three causes of weathering?
42 What is 'erosion'?
43 Can you explain how bits from one rock can end up forming new rock?

3.13

44 How are igneous rocks formed?
45 How are sedimentary rocks formed?
46 How are metamorphic rocks formed?
47 Can you give examples of an igneous, a sedimentary, and a metamorphic rock?

3.14

Test and check

Can you answer these questions? If not, the spread number tells you where to find out more.

1. What materials conduct electricity?
2. What do insulators do?
3. What do batteries do?

4.01

4. Can you draw a circuit with a bulb, battery, and switch in it? Can you add meters to measure the voltage across the battery, and the current?

4.02

5. Can you draw a circuit with a battery and two bulbs in series?
6. Can you draw a circuit with a battery and two bulbs in parallel?

4.03

7. Can you draw the magnetic field round a bar magnet?
8. How is an electromagnet made?
9. Can you explain how a relay works?

4.04

10. What is a newtonmeter used for?
11. What is measured in newtons?
12. Can you give an example of balanced forces?

4.05

13. When you push in a drawing pin, is the pressure greatest under your thumb, or under the point? Can you explain why?

4.06

14. How can you get a stronger turning effect from a spanner?
15. What is a 'centre of gravity'?

4.07

16. Can you explain what a 'speed of 10 metres per second' means?
17. Can you give an example of friction being useful?

4.08

18. What is measured in joules?
19. Can you give some examples of different forms of energy?

4.09

20. Can you think of something which has a high temperature but not much heat?
21. Can you give an example of something that stores energy?

4.10

22. Can you describe how a fuel-burning power station works?
23. What is 'hydroelectric power'?

4.11

24. What are 'fossil fuels'?
25. What are 'renewable' energy supplies?
26. Where does the energy in your food come from?

4.12

27. Can you explain how most of the world's energy comes from the Sun?

4.13

28. What are 'sound waves'?
29. How are sounds made?
30. Why do you see lightning before you hear it?

4.14

31. Can you describe how the ear works?
32. If a guitar string vibrates faster, how does this affect the sound? How do bigger vibrations affect the sound?

4.15

33. Can you draw a diagram showing how a ray of light reflects from a mirror?
34. What is refraction?

4.16

35. What materials are good conductors of heat?
36. What is a convection current?

4.17

37. Which surfaces radiate heat best?
38. How does a flask keep drinks hot?
39. Why do wet hands feel cold when you put them in a draught?

4.18

40. How would you produce a spectrum?
41. How could you make white using three beams of coloured light?
42. Why does a red book look red?

4.19

43. Why do we get day and night?
44. How long does the Earth take to go round the Sun?

4.20

45. How long does the Moon take to go round the Earth?
46. Can you describe some of the jobs that satellites are used for?

4.21

47. Can you describe how the planets move round the Sun?
48. Can you list the planets in order, starting with the one nearest the Sun?

4.22

1.01 Doing an investigation

Here is an investigation:

> Find out if sugar dissolves more quickly in
> hot water than in cold

You could do this like the girl on the right. But first, you need to know about the following:

▶ Key factors

In any investigation, you must decide what the **key factors** are. These are the things which affect what happens. In this investigation, the key factors are:

> type of sugar
> amount of sugar
> amount of water
> whether you stir or not
> temperature of water
> time for sugar to dissolve

I'm going to measure the time it takes sugar to dissolve in cold water — and then in hot.

▶ A fair test?

In the investigation, you must make sure that each test is fair.

For a fair test, you change just one factor (the temperature) and see how this affects one other factor (the time to dissolve):

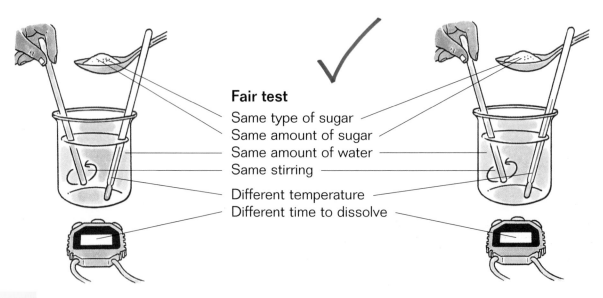

Fair test
Same type of sugar
Same amount of sugar
Same amount of water
Same stirring

Different temperature
Different time to dissolve

The test below is not a fair one. Lots of factors change as well as the temperature. So you cannot tell what effect the temperature is having:

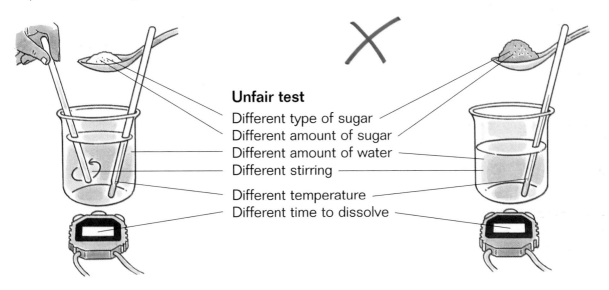

Unfair test
Different type of sugar
Different amount of sugar
Different amount of water
Different stirring
Different temperature
Different time to dissolve

Table.....

When you take readings, write them down in a table like this:

Temperature in °C	Time in seconds
20	75
30	52
40	36
50	

.....and graph

If you have several sets of readings, plot a graph. It will show you if the readings follow a pattern:

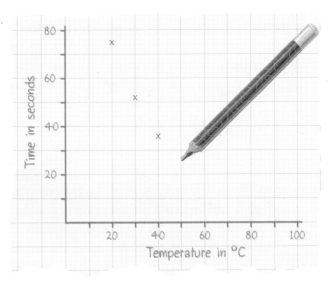

Conclusion

Your *conclusion* is what you found out. For example, from the points on the graph, your conclusion might be this:

The hotter the water, the less time it takes the sugar to dissolve

Made from cells

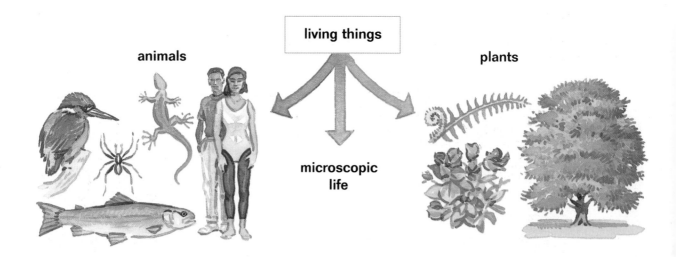

living things

animals

plants

microscopic life

Animals and plants are made from tiny bits called **cells**. There are millions of cells in your body. Most are so small that you would need a microscope to see them.

Animals and plants grow by making more cells. Cells are like tiny chemical factories. They take in food, make new materials for the body, and release energy when it is needed.

▶ Inside cells

This is what animal cells and plant cells are like inside:

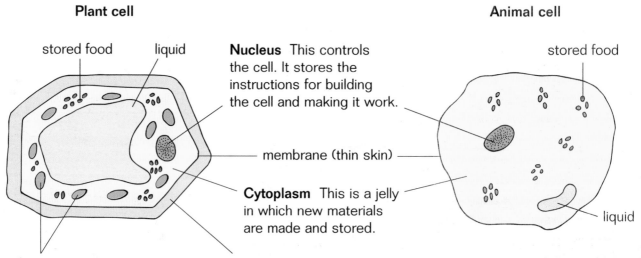

Plant cell

Animal cell

stored food   liquid

stored food

Nucleus This controls the cell. It stores the instructions for building the cell and making it work.

membrane (thin skin)

Cytoplasm This is a jelly in which new materials are made and stored.

liquid

Chloroplasts These contain **chlorophyll**, a green substance which soaks up the energy in the sunlight.

Cell wall This is made of tough cellulose. It makes stems and branches strong.

An animal cell does not have a cell wall or chloroplasts.

▶ Groups of cells

Cells have different shapes and sizes, depending on the jobs they have to do.

A group of similar cells is called **tissue**.

A group of tissues doing a particular job is called an **organ**. Eyes are organs, so are muscles.

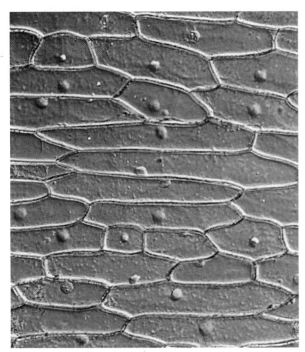

Onion cells, magnified 700 times

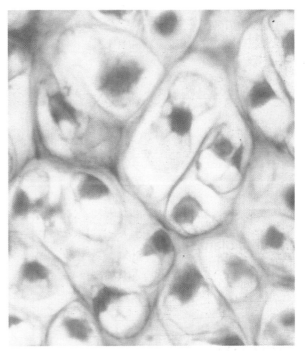

Human cheek cells, magnified 1500 times

1 *cells   animals   body   plants*

Copy the sentences below. Fill in the blanks, choosing words from those above:

Animals and ____ are living things.
Living things are made from ____.
There are millions of cells in your ____.

2 *tissue   nucleus   chloroplast   cell wall*

Write down the word above which goes with each of these:
a Controls what a cell does
b Takes in the energy in sunlight
c A group of similar cells.

3 Copy the diagrams on the right. Write in these labels:
animal   plant   nucleus   cell wall

4 Write down *two* things which are in a plant cell but not in an animal cell.

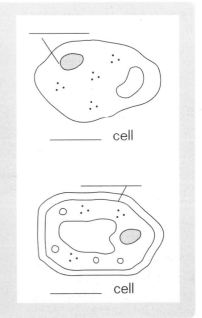

_____ cell

_____ cell

Making and using food

Animals have to find their food. But plants make their own.

A plant takes carbon dioxide gas from the air, and water from the soil.....

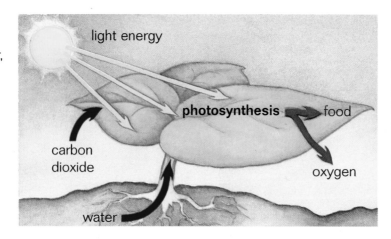

.....Using the energy in sunlight, it turns these into food (sugar) and oxygen gas.

Food-making using light energy is called *photosynthesis*.

▶ **Inside a plant**

Leaves are the plant's food-making factory. They soak up the Sun's energy. They also store food.

Water tubes carry water from the roots to the leaves.

Food tubes carry liquid food from the leaves to the parts that need it.

Stem This holds the plant upright

Minerals such as nitrates are needed for healthy growth.

Roots have tiny hairs which take water and minerals from the soil. Roots hold the plant in the ground. They also store food.

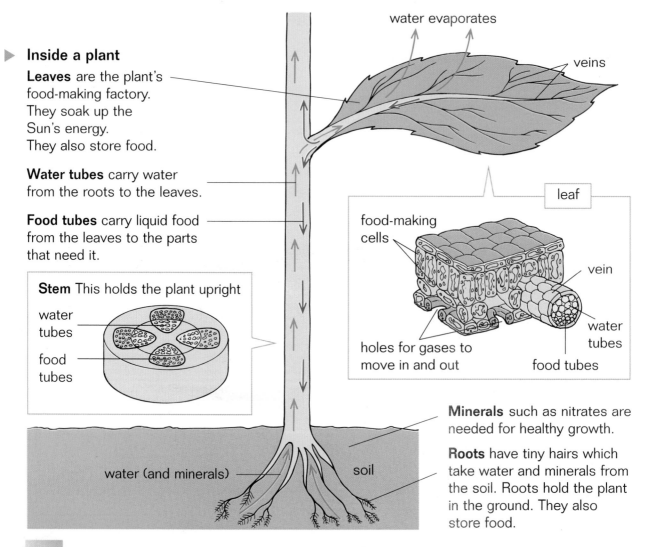

▶ Burning up food

Plants make and store food. Animals can get this food by eating plants. That is why you eat fruit and vegetables.

To get energy, animals 'burn up' their food. For this, they need oxygen from the air. That is why you have to breathe in air.

Plants also need oxygen to burn up their food. But they make more oxygen than they can use.

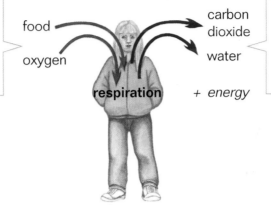

food

oxygen

respiration

carbon dioxide

water

+ energy

Burning up food makes carbon dioxide gas and water. So these things are in the air you breathe out.

Getting energy by burning up food is called *respiration*.

▶ Gas changes in the air

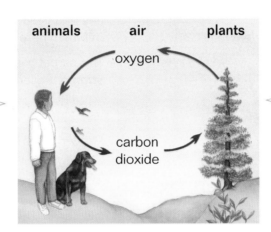

animals   air   plants

oxygen

carbon dioxide

Animals use up oxygen and make carbon dioxide.

Plants use up carbon dioxide and make oxygen.

Plants replace the oxygen that animals use up.

---

1 Copy the diagram on the right.
  Shade in the parts where the plant makes its food.
  Label them 'Food is made here'.

2 *sunlight   oxygen   carbon dioxide   leaves*
  Copy the sentences below. Fill in the blanks, choosing words from those above. (You may use the same word more than once.)
  To make their food, plants use the energy in ____.
  Plants take in ____ gas and give out ____ gas.
  Animals take in ____ gas and give out ____ gas.
  To burn up their food, animals need ____.

3 Describe how water gets to the leaves of a plant.

4 Describe how a plant gets the minerals it needs.

5 Describe how gases get in and out of a leaf.

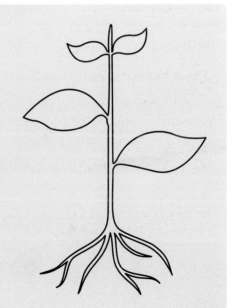

Flowers

New plants grow from seeds.
Seeds come from flowers.

Flowers have **sex cells** inside them. To make a seed, a **male cell** must join with a **female cell**.

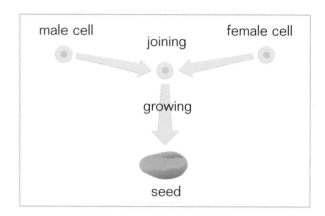

Parts of a flower

Stamen This has a bulge at the end called an **anther**. It holds thousands of tiny grains of **pollen**. There is a male cell in each grain.

When the **anther** splits open, the pollen grains fall out.

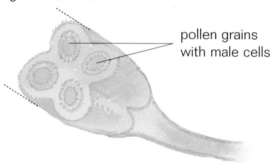

pollen grains with male cells

Carpel This has an **ovary** inside, where tiny eggs grow. The eggs are called **ovules**. There is a female cell in each one.

The carpel has a sticky end called a **stigma**. Pollen can stick to this.

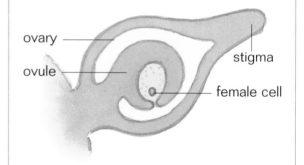

Petal This may be brightly coloured to attract insects.

Nectary This contains nectar, a sugary food for insects.

▶ Pollinating flowers

Before a male cell can join with a female cell, pollen must get across to a stigma and stick to it. This is called **pollination**. Usually, the pollen is carried across to another flower.

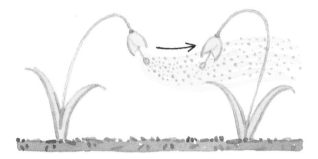

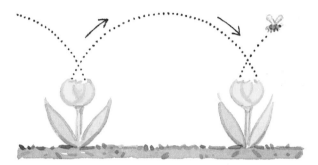

Some flowers are pollinated by wind Their flowers have stamens that hang out in the wind. When their pollen is blown away, some lands on other flowers.

Some flowers are pollinated by insects The insects are attracted by the scent or bright colours. As they search for nectar, they get covered in pollen and carry it to other flowers.

After pollination, the male and female sex cells can join. To find out how, see the next page.

1 *pollen   ovules   nectar   petal*

Copy the diagram below. Fill in the blanks, choosing words from those above:

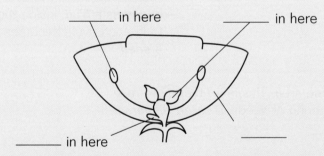

_____ in here   _____ in here

_____ in here   _____

2 *pollination   male   female   flowering*

Copy the sentences below. Fill in the blanks, choosing words from those above:

In each ovule, there is a ____ cell.
In each pollen grain, there is a ____ cell.
When pollen sticks to a stigma, this is called ____.

3 Look at the photograph on the right.
   a Explain why the flower is brightly coloured.
   b Explain what the bee is doing.
   c Explain how a bee pollinates flowers.

Fruits and seeds

▶ Fertilization

After pollination, when pollen grains stick to a stigma, this is what happens:

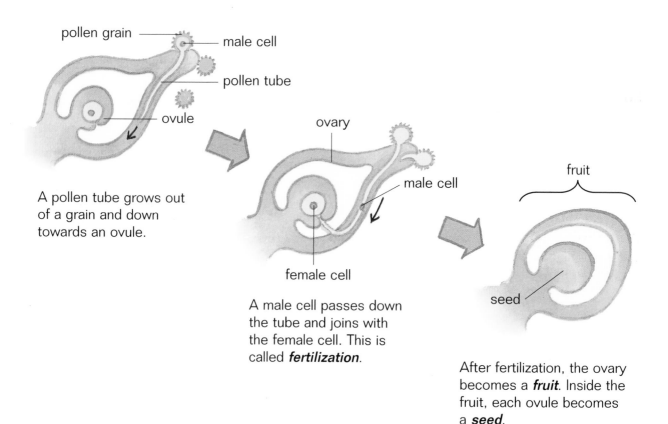

A pollen tube grows out of a grain and down towards an ovule.

A male cell passes down the tube and joins with the female cell. This is called **fertilization**.

After fertilization, the ovary becomes a **fruit**. Inside the fruit, each ovule becomes a **seed**.

▶ Scattering seeds

Flowers try to scatter their seeds over a wide area. This is so that more may survive and grow into new plants. The scattering of seeds is called **dispersal**.

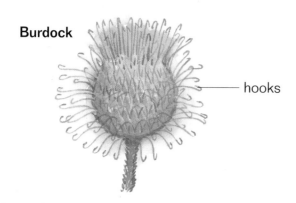

Some fruits and seeds have hooks so that they are carried by animals.

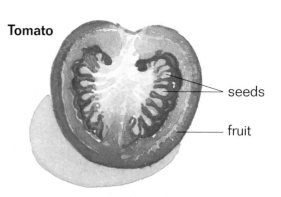

Some fruits are eaten by animals. The seeds come out with their droppings.

Sycamore

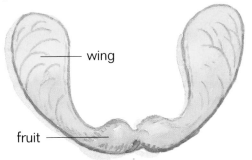

wing

fruit

Some fruits and seeds are shaped so that they can be carried by the wind.

Pea

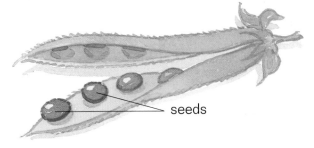

seeds

Some seeds are in pods. When dry, these pop open and flick out the seeds.

▶ Germination

A seed has a store of food inside it.

When a seed starts to grow, this is called *germination*.

To germinate, a seed needs.....

water	warmth	air

When a seed germinates:
A tiny **shoot** grows upwards towards the light.
A tiny **root** grows downwards into the soil.

Germination of a broad bean

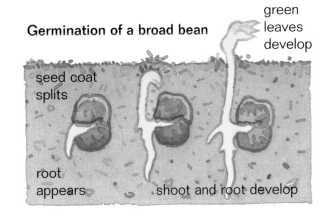

green leaves develop

seed coat splits

root appears

shoot and root develop

---

1 *germination   fertilization   scattering*

Copy the sentences below. Fill in the blanks, choosing words from those above:

   A male cell joining with a female cell is called ____.
   A seed starting to grow is called ____.

2 Copy these sentences in the correct order:

   A male cell joins with a female cell.
   Pollen sticks to a stigma.
   A male cell passes down the pollen tube.
   The ovule becomes a seed.
   Pollen is carried from one flower to another.
   A pollen tube grows down towards an ovule.

3 Write down *three* things which seeds need to germinate.

4 Look at the diagram on the right.
   Describe how you think the seeds are scattered.

Dandelion

fruit

Organs of the body

An **organ** is any part of the body with a special job to do. The next page shows some of the main organs of the human body. The organs are all made of tiny cells.

▶ **The body at work**

Your body takes in food, water, and oxygen. The blood carries them to all your organs. There, the cells use them for growth and for getting energy.

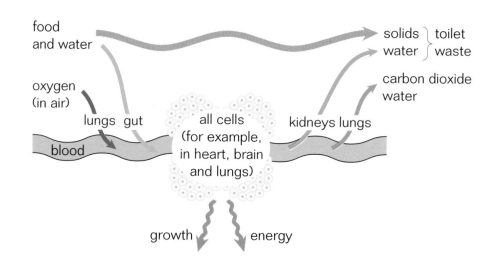

Your body gives out waste. Some is unused food that goes right through you. But cells also make waste, such as carbon dioxide and water. The blood carries these to the organs that get rid of them:

The **kidneys** get rid of water (through your bladder).

The **lungs** get rid of carbon dioxide and water (as damp air).

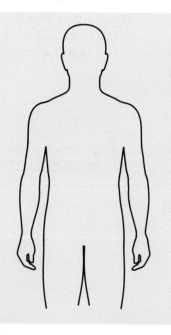

1 Here are some organs:

    stomach   lung   heart   kidney   bladder

Write down the organ which does each of these:
a Stores food when you eat it.
b Puts oxygen into the blood.
c Pumps blood through all the organs.
d Cleans the blood by making urine.

2 Copy the diagram on the left.
Draw in the organ which controls the whole body.
Label it, using one of the words below.
Draw in an organ which gets rid of carbon dioxide.
Label it, using one of the words below.

    lung   kidney   heart   brain

3 Write down *three* things that the body must take in.

4 Write down *two* ways in which the body can get rid of water.

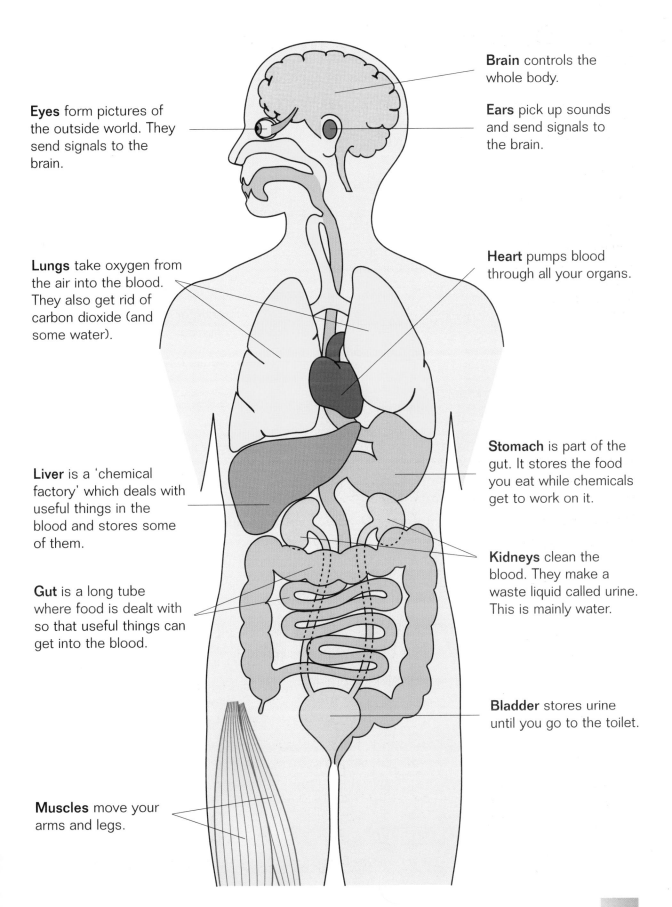

Brain controls the whole body.

Eyes form pictures of the outside world. They send signals to the brain.

Ears pick up sounds and send signals to the brain.

Lungs take oxygen from the air into the blood. They also get rid of carbon dioxide (and some water).

Heart pumps blood through all your organs.

Stomach is part of the gut. It stores the food you eat while chemicals get to work on it.

Liver is a 'chemical factory' which deals with useful things in the blood and stores some of them.

Kidneys clean the blood. They make a waste liquid called urine. This is mainly water.

Gut is a long tube where food is dealt with so that useful things can get into the blood.

Bladder stores urine until you go to the toilet.

Muscles move your arms and legs.

2.06 Bones, joints, and muscles

▶ **The skeleton**

Your body is held up by a **skeleton**. This has several jobs to do:

Support The skeleton lets you stand upright. It also supports organs inside you.

Protection The skeleton protects many organs.

Movement The skeleton has joints so that you can move bits of your body. The joints are moved by muscles.

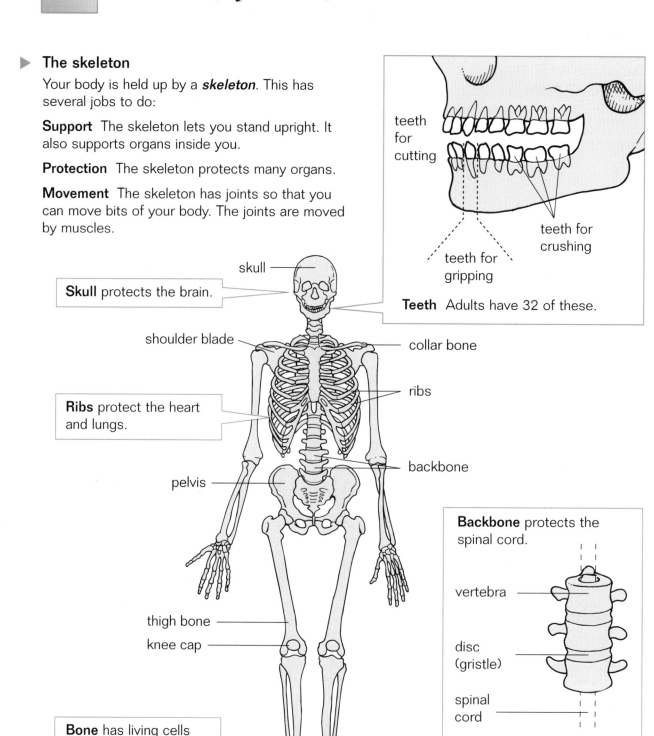

teeth for cutting

teeth for crushing

teeth for gripping

Teeth Adults have 32 of these.

skull

| **Skull** protects the brain. |

shoulder blade

collar bone

ribs

| **Ribs** protect the heart and lungs. |

backbone

pelvis

thigh bone

knee cap

| **Bone** has living cells with hard minerals around them. Calcium is the main mineral in bone. |

Backbone protects the spinal cord.

vertebra

disc (gristle)

spinal cord

The backbone is really lots of bones with gristle discs between them. The **discs** let the backbone bend a little. They also absorb the jolts.

Joints and muscles

To bend a joint, a muscle contracts (gets shorter). But it cannot get longer again by itself. So muscles are arranged in pairs. One muscle pulls the joint one way, the other pulls it back again.

Raising arm

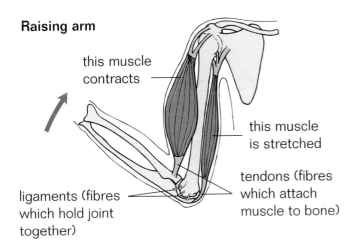

this muscle contracts

this muscle is stretched

tendons (fibres which attach muscle to bone)

ligaments (fibres which hold joint together)

Lowering arm

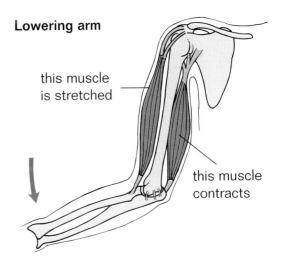

this muscle is stretched

this muscle contracts

Controlling muscles

To control your muscles, signals are sent along **nerves**.

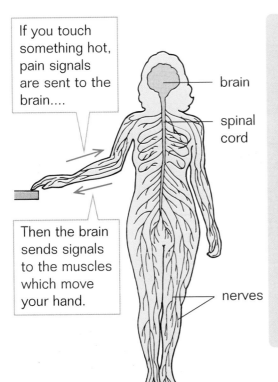

If you touch something hot, pain signals are sent to the brain....

Then the brain sends signals to the muscles which move your hand.

brain

spinal cord

nerves

1 *backbone   skull   ribs   pelvis*

Copy the sentences below. Fill in the blanks choosing words from those above:

The ____ protects the brain.
The ____ protect the heart and lungs.
The ____ protects the spinal cord.

2 Here are some parts of the body:

nerves   muscles   discs   teeth

Write down which of these do the following:
a Cut, grip, or crush food.
b Move joints.
c Carry signals to or from the brain.

3 Copy and complete these sentences:

The main mineral in bone is....
Fibres which hold joints together are called.....
Fibres which attach muscle to bone are called.....

Dealing with food

▶ The gut

This is a long tube that runs from your mouth down through your body. This is where food is dealt with.

The main parts of the gut are:

mouth, gullet, stomach, small intestine, large intestine.

When you eat, the useful things in your food must get into your blood. But first, they must be changed into a liquid. This is called **digestion**.

In your gut, there are special chemicals for digesting food. These are called **enzymes**.

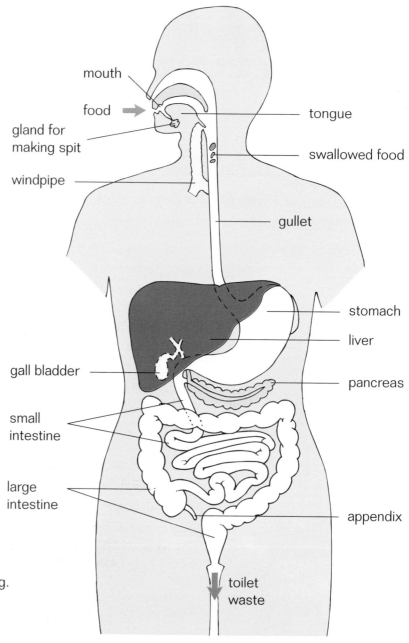

mouth

food

gland for making spit

windpipe

tongue

swallowed food

gullet

stomach

liver

gall bladder

pancreas

small intestine

large intestine

appendix

toilet waste

Your gut is over 6 metres long.

▶ What happens to your food

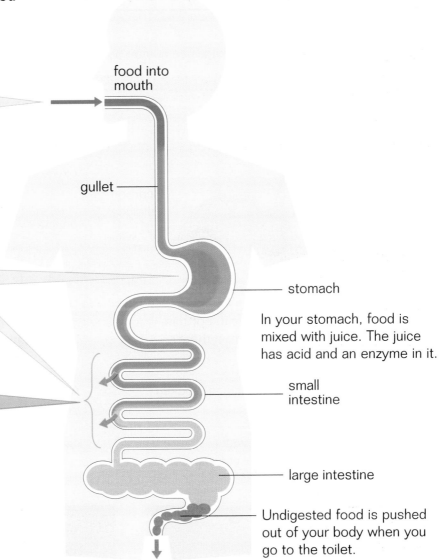

Digestion
Digestion starts in your mouth. When you chew, food gets mixed with spit. The spit has an enzyme in it. This changes solid bits of starch into liquid sugar.

Enzymes turn food into liquid. This mainly happens in the stomach and small intestine.

Absorption
Digested food (liquid) seeps into the blood. This mainly happens in the small intestine.

food into mouth

gullet

stomach

In your stomach, food is mixed with juice. The juice has acid and an enzyme in it.

small intestine

large intestine

Undigested food is pushed out of your body when you go to the toilet.

---

1 *absorption   digestion   enzymes   blood*

Copy the sentences below. Fill in the blanks, choosing words from those above.

The useful things in your food must get into your ____.
Changing solid food into liquid is called ____.
Your food is digested by chemicals called ____.

2 Copy these sentences in the correct order:

In the stomach, food is mixed with acid and an enzyme.
Undigested food passes through the large intestine.
Food is chewed and mixed with spit.
Undigested food goes down the toilet.
In the small intestine, digested food seeps into the blood.
Food passes down the gullet.

The human engine

A car has an engine to move it along. The human body also has an engine – its muscles.

	Car engine	Human engine
	fuel (petrol or diesel) oxygen engine → carbon dioxide water	fuel (food) oxygen engine → carbon dioxide water
Fuel	Petrol or diesel A car engine gets energy from its fuel by **burning** it. For this, it needs oxygen from the air.	Food The human engine gets energy from its food by **respiration** – a type of burning without any flames. For this, it needs oxygen from the air.
Oxygen supply	Air (containing oxygen) sucked into the engine.	Air (containing oxygen) breathed into the lungs.
Exhaust gases	carbon dioxide, water + small amounts of polluting gases	carbon dioxide, water

There is water in the exhaust gases from a car engine. On a cold day, you can see it as clouds of steam.

Like an engine, the human body also gives out exhaust gases. The body's 'exhaust pipe' is the mouth.

▶ Blood around the body

Blood brings food and oxygen to the cells in your muscles and other organs. It also takes away their waste carbon dioxide and water.

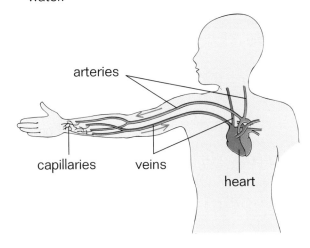

arteries

capillaries   veins

heart

The heart pumps blood round the body through tubes called arteries, capillaries, and veins.

Arteries carry blood away from the heart.

Capillaries are thousands of narrow tubes running from arteries to veins. Every cell in the body is close to a capillary so that blood can bring the cell the things it needs.

Veins carry blood back to the heart.

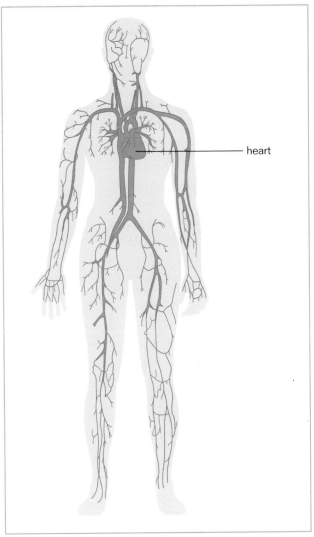

heart

Some of the arteries and veins in the human body.

---

1 Choosing words from the list on the right, write down:
   a two things taken in by a car engine for burning
   b two things taken in by the human body for respiration
   c two things coming out of a car's exhaust pipe
   d two things breathed out by the human body.

2 Here are three types of blood tube:
   vein   capillary   artery

   Write down which type does each of these:
   a Carries blood away from the heart
   b Carries blood back to the heart
   c Carries blood close to cells.

3 Explain why your muscles need a supply of blood.

petrol

carbon dioxide

water

food

oxygen

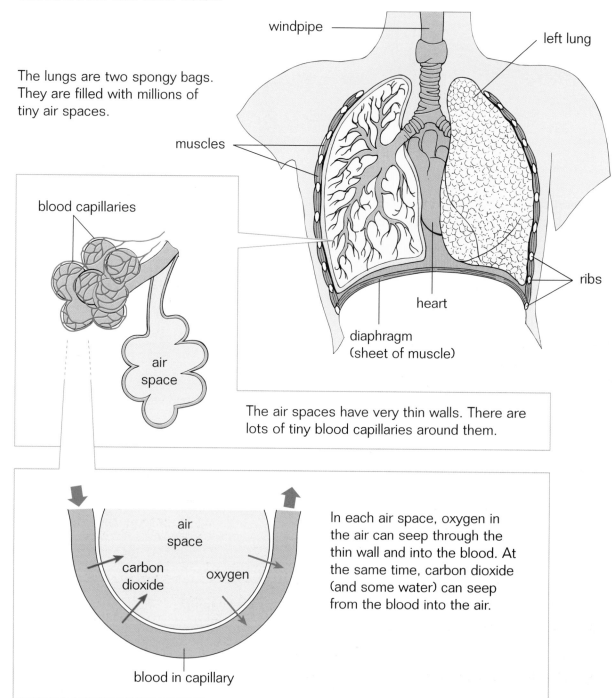

The lungs and breathing

▶ The lungs

The cells of your body use up oxygen. At the same time, they make carbon dioxide (and water) which they do not want. The job of the lungs is to put oxygen into the blood, and remove carbon dioxide (and some water).

windpipe

left lung

The lungs are two spongy bags. They are filled with millions of tiny air spaces.

muscles

blood capillaries

ribs

air space

heart

diaphragm (sheet of muscle)

The air spaces have very thin walls. There are lots of tiny blood capillaries around them.

air space

carbon dioxide

oxygen

In each air space, oxygen in the air can seep through the thin wall and into the blood. At the same time, carbon dioxide (and some water) can seep from the blood into the air.

blood in capillary

▶ Breathing

As you breathe in and out, your lungs get bigger and smaller. Some of the old air in your lungs is replaced by new. There is an *exchange* of carbon dioxide and oxygen.

Breathing in

ribs pulled upwards and outwards by muscles

lungs fill with air

diaphragm pulled downwards by muscles

Breathing out

air pushed out from lungs

diaphragm relaxes

Smoking stops your lungs working properly. Tobacco smoke contains harmful chemicals which can irritate or destroy lung tissue, make air spaces clog up, and cause cancer.

1 *rib   lung   heart   diaphragm   windpipe*
Copy the diagram on the right. Fill in the blanks using the labels above.

2 *diaphragm   air   water   blood   lungs   ribs*
Copy these sentences. Fill in the blanks, choosing words from those above:

When you breathe in, your ____ move upwards and outwards, your ____ moves downwards, and your ____ fill with ____. In your lungs, the tiny air spaces are surrounded by ____ capillaries.

3 In your lungs, what gas goes into the blood?

4 In your lungs, what gas comes out of the blood?

5 Explain why you have to keep breathing in and out.

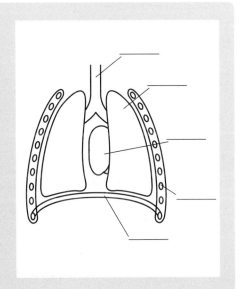

Making human life

A baby grows from a tiny cell in its mother. The cell is made when a tiny egg, or **ovum**, inside the mother is fertilized by a **sperm** from the father. The sperm and egg join together to form a single cell.

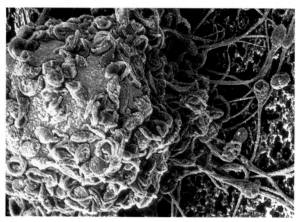

Sperms around an egg, magnified 1000 times

▶ Puberty

This is the time when a girl can first become a mother, and a boy can first become a father. For girls, the age is often 12–14. For boys it is often 14–16. But later than this is quite normal.

▶ A woman's sex system

Ovulation About every 28 days, a woman releases an egg from one of her **ovaries**. This is called **ovulation**. The tiny egg moves down the **egg tube** and into the **uterus** (womb).

Lining growth The lining of the womb thickens, and blood capillaries grow in it. The womb is now ready for a fertilized egg.

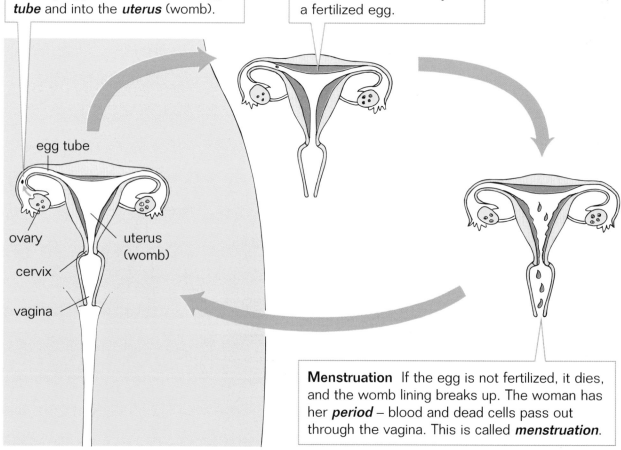

egg tube

ovary

cervix

vagina

uterus (womb)

Menstruation If the egg is not fertilized, it dies, and the womb lining breaks up. The woman has her **period** – blood and dead cells pass out through the vagina. This is called **menstruation**.

▶ A man's sex system

A man makes sperms in his **testicles**.

Before sperms leave his body, they are mixed with a liquid. Sperms and liquid are called **semen**. Semen comes out of the man's penis.

▶ Fertilization

When a man and woman have sex, the man's penis goes stiff and is put in the woman's vagina. Then semen shoots out of his penis. There are millions of sperms, but only one can fertilize the egg by joining with it.

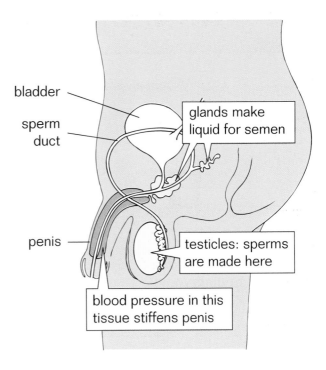

bladder

sperm duct

glands make liquid for semen

penis

testicles: sperms are made here

blood pressure in this tissue stiffens penis

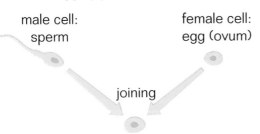

male cell: sperm

female cell: egg (ovum)

joining

fertilized egg

▶ Birth control

Parents may want a small family. If so, they may decide to use **contraception** (birth control). Here are some of the methods:

Condom This is a rubber cover which fits over the man's penis. It traps sperms. It is only reliable if used with a cream which kills sperms.

Diaphragm This is a rubber cover which fits over the woman's cervix. It stops sperms reaching the womb. It is only reliable if used with a cream which kills sperms.

The pill The woman takes this every day. It stops her ovaries releasing eggs. It is reliable, but can cause heart, liver, and breast disease.

Natural method The woman does tests to find out when ovulation is close, and does not have sex near that time. This method can be used by people who think that other kinds of birth control are wrong.

---

1 Copy these sentences in the correct order, starting with the one which tells you about *ovulation*:

> The woman has her period.
> If the egg is not fertilized, the womb lining breaks up.
> An ovary releases an egg, and the womb lining thickens.

2 *ovaries   testicles   fertilization   menstruation*

From the above words, choose one for each of these:
a Sperms are made in these.
b Eggs are released from these.
c A sperm joining with an egg.

Growing to be born

Actual sizes

Fertilized egg

Embryo

...at 4 weeks

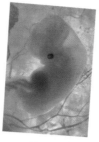

...at 7 weeks

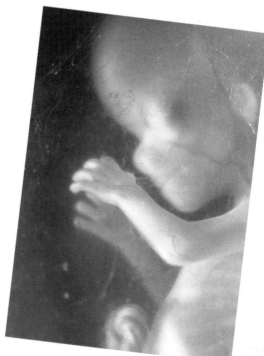

Fetus at 14 weeks

▶ **From egg to embryo**

If a human egg is fertilized, it grows into a tiny ball of cells. This is called an **embryo**. It sinks into the lining of the womb and starts to grow into a baby.

▶ **The growing embryo**

After six weeks, the embryo has a heart and a brain. It lies in a bag of watery liquid which protects it from jolts and bumps.

The embryo cannot eat or breath, so it must get all the things it needs from its mother's blood. It does this through an organ called the **placenta**. This grows into the womb lining.

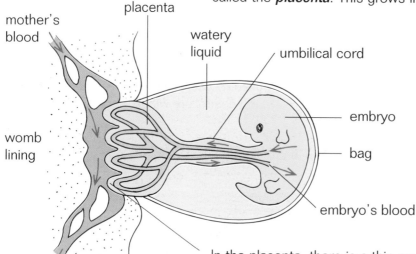

The embryo is linked to the placenta by an **umbilical cord**.

In the placenta, there is a thin membrane (sheet) between the mother's blood and the embryo's. The bloods do not mix, but food, oxygen, and other things can pass between them.

At 8 weeks, the embryo is beginning to look like a tiny baby. It is now called a **fetus**.

▶ Birth

This is what normally happens:

9 months before birth
   Fertilization.
   Embryo starts to grow.

A few days before birth
The baby turns head down.

Just before birth
   Contractions start – muscles round
   the womb squeeze up.
   The cervix starts to open.
   The baby's head passes into the vagina.
   The bag bursts and the watery liquid
   runs out.

Birth
   Contractions push the baby out.
   The baby's lungs fill with air. From now
   on, the baby must take in its own
   oxygen and food.

Just after birth
   Contractions push out the placenta
   (the 'afterbirth').
   A doctor or nurse cuts the umbilical
   cord. The remains of the cord will
   shrivel away to leave the 'belly button'.

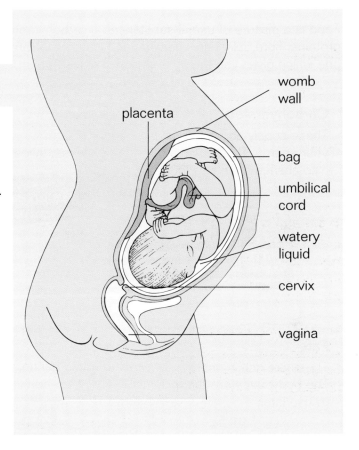

placenta

womb wall

bag

umbilical cord

watery liquid

cervix

vagina

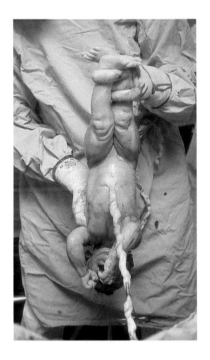

1 *umbilical cord   embryo*
   placenta   bag of watery liquid
   Write down which of the above things does each of these:
   a Protects a baby in the womb from jolts and bumps.
   b Links the baby to the placenta.
   c Grows into the womb lining so that things can
      pass between the mother's blood and the baby's.

2 Copy these sentences in the correct order.
      The baby turns head down.
      The umbilical cord is cut.
      Contractions push the afterbirth out.
      The embryo grows into a baby.
      The embryo sinks into the womb lining.
      Contractions push the baby out.

3 Explain how a baby gets its food and oxygen
   when it is in the womb.

The food you need

Food is a mixture of useful substances – carbohydrates, fats, proteins, fibre, minerals, vitamins, and water. A *balanced* diet is one which gives you the right amounts of all of them.

Carbohydrates

These supply about half of your energy. The body may also change them into fats.

Examples

Sugar in...
jams, cakes, sweets, fruit

Starch in...
potatoes, rice, bread, flour

Fats

These are rich in energy. The body can store them to use later.

Examples

Butter, margarine, vegetable oil, lard, meat, cheese

Proteins

These are for body-building. You need them for growth and for replacing dead cells.

Examples

Meat, eggs, fish, milk, cheese, bread

Minerals

Your body needs small amounts of these.

Examples

Calcium (for making bones and teeth) from cheese, milk
Iron (for making blood) from liver, eggs, bread

Vitamins

Your body needs small amounts of these.

Examples

Vitamin A	**Vitamin B$_1$**	**Vitamin B$_2$**	**Vitamin C**	**Vitamin D**
Margarine, butter, liver, carrots, green vegetables, fish oil	Yeast, bread, meat, milk, potatoes	Milk, liver, eggs, cheese	Blackcurrants, green vegetables, oranges	Margarine, eggs, fish oil

Fibre

You can't digest fibre. But it is good for you because it helps food pass through your gut more easily.

Examples

Vegetables, cereals, bread

Water

You need about a litre of water every day – more if it is hot or you are very active.

Examples

Drinks, fruits and other foods with water in

---

1 *proteins   carbohydrates   fats   vitamins*

Copy these sentences. Fill in the blanks, choosing words from those above.

You need ____ and ____ for energy.
You need ____ for growth.

2 Copy the chart on the right.
The tick shows that bread has lots of carbohydrate in it. Put in more ticks to complete the chart.

Food ▼	carbo-hydrate	fat	protein
bread	✓		
milk			
cheese			

3 Write down *two* foods with *calcium* in.

4 Write down *two* foods with *fibre* in.

5 Write down *two* foods with *vitamin C* in.

6 Copy and complete these sentences:
  a Your body needs calcium because......
  b Your body needs fibre because....

2.13 Germs and diseases

▶ Microbes

Microbes are tiny living things that can only be seen with a microscope. There are billions in the air, soil, water, and our bodies. The harmful ones are called **germs**. They cause disease.

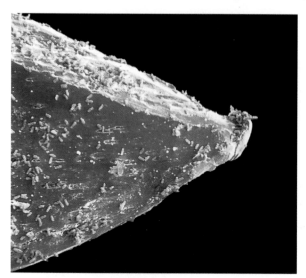

Bacteria on the tip of a hypodermic needle, magnified 400 times.

Bacteria and viruses are microbes:

Bacteria are living cells. They can *multiply* very quickly – until there are millions of them.

Diseases caused by bacteria – examples
Sore throats, pneumonia, food poisoning.

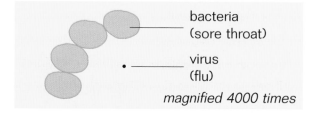

bacteria
(sore throat)

virus
(flu)

magnified 4000 times

Viruses are smaller than bacteria. They invade your cells and stop them working properly.

Diseases caused by viruses – examples
Flu, chicken-pox, colds

▶ Fighting disease

If germs get into your body, your white blood cells attack them. Some cells make chemicals called **antibodies** which kill germs.

If you have had chicken-pox, you probably won't catch it again. You are **immune** to it. That is because you already have antibodies for the disease, so you are ready for the next attack.

Medicines help fight disease:

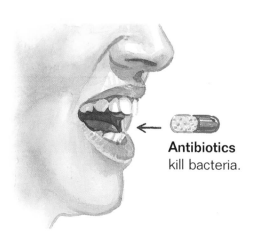

Antibiotics
kill bacteria.

Vaccines have weak or dead germs put in them. Your white blood cells make antibodies for these germs. So, when the real disease strikes, your body is ready to fight it.

▶ Spreading germs

An invasion of germs is called an *infection*.
Germs can spread like this:

Droplets in the air When you cough or sneeze, you spray droplets into the air. These carry germs which other people breathe in.

Example
Catching flu or a cold.

Animals Insects may leave germs on food. Or they may leave germs in the blood when they bite.

Example
Blood-sucking mosquitoes spreading malaria.

Contact You can pick up some germs by touching an infected person or thing.

Example
Catching chicken-pox.

Dirty food and water Germs from toilet waste can get into food and water.

Example
Handling food after using the toilet.

1 *germs   infection   vaccine   immune   antibodies   antibiotics*
Copy these sentences. Fill in the blanks, choosing words from those above.
  a Harmful microbes are called ____.
  b An invasion of germs is called an ____.
  c If you are ____ to a disease, you won't catch it again.
  d Some white blood cells make ____ which kill germs.
  e A ____ has weak or dead germs in it.

2 Look at the diagram on the right. Write down *three* ways in which germs might get into the boy's body.

3 Explain why you should wash your hands after using the toilet.

2.14 Healthy living

To help your health, you need to do these things:

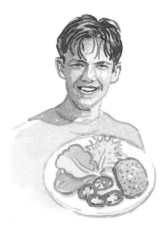
Eat sensibly

Take plenty of exercise

Avoid health risks

▶ Diet

● If you do not eat enough fruit and vegetables, you may not get enough vitamins and fibre.

● Too little fibre makes you constipated and may cause disease in the gut.

● Too much fat makes you overweight and may cause heart disease.

▶ Health risks

Smoking This causes heart attacks, blocked arteries, lung cancer, and difficult breathing.

Solvents These are in glue and paint. Sniffing them is very dangerous. It damages the lungs and brain.

Alcohol This slows your reactions. Heavy drinking damages the liver, heart, and stomach.

Drugs Some of these are *addictive*. When the body gets used to them, it cannot do without them.

AIDS

AIDS is a disease that can't yet be cured. It is caused by a virus called **HIV**.

People with the virus are **HIV positive**. But it may be many years before they develop AIDS.

HIV attacks white blood cells, so the body can't defend itself against disease.

HIV can only be passed to others in three ways:

● When two people are having sex.
● By blood-to-blood contact.
● From an infected mother to her unborn baby.

If a man wears a condom while having sex, there is less chance of HIV being passed on.

▶ Health before birth

A mother must look after her baby *before* it is born.

Smoking If she smokes, her baby may be born underweight.

Alcohol If she drinks alcohol, her baby may be harmed. Also, it may be born too early.

German measles (rubella) If she catches German measles in the first three months of pregnancy, her baby may be born deaf, blind, or with heart trouble.

That is why girls are given injections to stop them catching German measles.

---

1 The sentences below have got the wrong endings.
Write them out so that the correct parts go together.

Smoking is bad for you because...   ...it helps prevent constipation.

A pregnant woman shouldn't smoke because...   ...it contains vitamins and fibre.

Too much alcohol is bad for you because...   ...they damage your lungs and brain.

Solvents are bad for you because...   ...it causes lung cancer and heart disease.

Fibre is good for you because...   ...her baby may be born underweight.

Fruit is good for you because...   ...it damages your liver.

2 Explain why girls are given injections to stop them catching German measles.

2.15 Variation

Look at these two animals.

They have some features which are *similar*:

They have some features which are *different*:

- One beak
- Two eyes
- Lots of feathers

- Length of beak
- Position of eyes
- Colour of feathers

Scientists use *similar* features to put things into groups.

The two animals are both in a group called **birds**.

Scientists use *different* features to tell things apart.

One bird is an **owl**. The other bird is a **gull**.

▶ For more about sorting animals into groups, see the next spread, 2.16.

Varying features

Even animals of the same kind are never exactly alike. Look at the family of dogs in the photograph on the right. Their features are not all the same. There is **variation** from one dog to another.

All animals and plants show variation. For example, here are some human features which can vary:

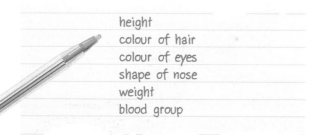

height
colour of hair
colour of eyes
shape of nose
weight
blood group

Your different features are sometimes called your **characteristics**.

Like all living things, these dogs show variation.

Features passed on...

Some features are *inherited*. You are born with them. There were passed on to you by your parents.

Tim and Jim are 'identical twins'. They inherited the same features from their parents. For example, they inherited their mother's black hair.

...and not passed on

Some features are not inherited. You are not born with them. You get them as you go through life.

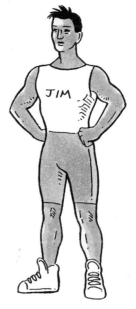

Tim and Jim are not *exactly* alike. Jim has bigger muscles because he trains in the gym. He did not inherit his big muscles. They will not be passed on to his children.

Selective breeding

People try to breed animals with special features: for example, dogs with long hair, or horses that can run fast. To do this, they select the animals which will mate (have sex). This is called *selective breeding*. The idea is that the 'babies' may inherit the best features of both parents. Selective breeding is also used with plants to get better crops.

1 Look at the two animals on the right.
   a Write down *three* features they have which are *similar*
   b Write down *three* features they have which are *different*.

2 Look at the dogs on the left. Write down *three* features which show variation.

3 A person can have features which are not inherited. Write down one example.

4 Write down one example of selective breeding.

Sorting into groups

Scientists think that all living things are related. They sort them into groups with similar features. The biggest groups of all are called **kingdoms**. You can see them on the next page.

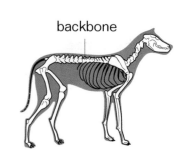

backbone

▶ **Animals with backbones**

In the animal kingdom, animals with backbones are called **vertebrates**. There are five main groups:

Fish

Fins
Covered in scales
Live in water
Gills for breathing
Lay eggs
Body temperature changes
Examples Shark, herring, cod

Reptiles

Covered in dry scales
Most live on land
Lungs for breathing
Lay eggs
Body temperature changes
Examples Crocodile, tortoise, lizard

Amphibians

Covered in moist skin
Live in water and on land
Adults have lungs for breathing
Lay eggs, usually in water
Body temperature changes
Examples Newt, toad, frog

Birds

Covered in feathers
Lungs for breathing
Lay eggs
Steady body temperature
Examples Robin, penguin, blackbird

Mammals

Covered in hairy skin
Lungs for breathing
Most give birth to babies and do not lay eggs
Mother makes milk for babies
Steady body temperature
Examples Cat, human, whale, mouse

Feature ▼	Fish	Amphibians	Reptiles	Birds	Mammals
backbone					
lungs					
scales					
feathers					
hair					
lay eggs					
born as babies					✓
steady body temperature					

1 Copy the table on the left. The tick shows that most mammals have babies.

  Put in more ticks to complete the table.

  Put a big 'H' at the bottom of the column that humans are in.

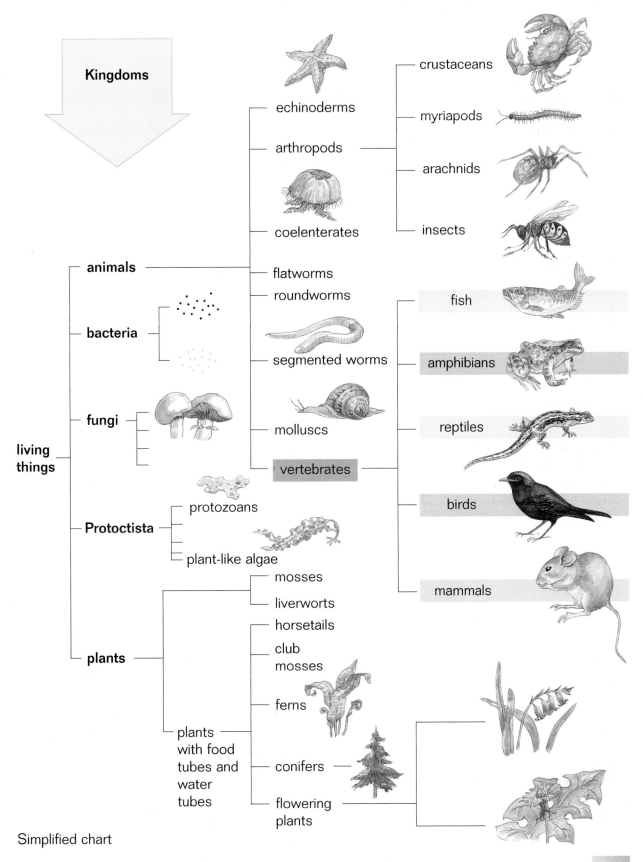

Kingdoms

crustaceans

echinoderms

myriapods

arthropods

arachnids

insects

coelenterates

animals

flatworms

roundworms

fish

bacteria

amphibians

segmented worms

fungi

reptiles

molluscs

vertebrates

birds

protozoans

Protoctista

plant-like algae

mammals

mosses

liverworts

horsetails

club mosses

plants

ferns

plants with food tubes and water tubes

conifers

flowering plants

living things

Simplified chart

Living places

▶ Habitats

The place where an animal or plant lives is called its *habitat*. It is usually shared with other animals and plants. It must provide food, shelter, and the right conditions for life.

A frog's habitat is in and around a pond, where it is wet and shady. A frog needs these conditions to stop its skin drying out.

More animals and plants live in some habitats than in others. Here are some of the *factors* which affect living things and their habitats:

Climate Some places are hotter, wetter, or windier than others.

Other living things

Plants need water and light. They stop other plants getting them.

Animals need food. They eat plants and other animals.

Humans take over land for crops. They dig soil and cut down trees.

Days and seasons It is warmer and lighter in the day than at night. It is warmer in summer than in winter.

Landscape It is more sheltered in a valley than on a hill or the coast.

Soil Clay soils hold water. Sandy soils dry quickly. Some soils have lime in them. Others have acid. This affects how plants grow.

▶ Pollution

Pollution can harm living things and their habitats. Humans cause pollution. Here are some examples:

Harmful gases These come from power stations, factories, cars, and trucks.

Factory waste Poisonous chemicals may be dumped into rivers or the sea.

Sewage This is often dumped at sea. The germs in it are harmful to health.

▶ Sustainable development

Humans need fuels, and materials such as metals, stone, and wood. Getting and using these things causes pollution, and destroys the habitats of other animal and plants. That is why we should try to use things which do not harm the environment, and are replaced naturally or can be grown again. This idea is called **sustainable development**. Here is an example:

Timber is needed for house-building, furniture, and papermaking. By planting fast-growing pine trees like those on the right, new wood can be grown at the same rate as old wood is used.

---

1 *human   polar bear   frog   camel*

Write down the animal above which does each of these:
  a Lives in a wet, shady habitat
  b Lives in a cold, icy habitat
  c Causes pollution.

2 Write down *two* things done by humans which can damage the habitats of other animals and plants.

3 Copy and complete these sentences with your own words:
  a A plant can stop another plant growing because...
  b An animal can stop a plant growing because...

Features for living

Animals and plants have special features to help them survive in their habitat. They are *adapted* to their way of life.

▶ **Surviving the winter**

This robin fluffs up its feathers when cold. The feathers trap air like a sleeping bag or duvet.

Many trees lose their leaves in the autumn. Without leaves, they need less water. So they can survive when the ground is frozen.

▶ **Camouflage**

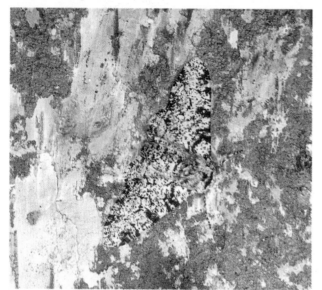

Peppered moths are difficult to see against a tree. So they probably won't get eaten by a bird.

There is a leaf insect in this photograph. Can you find it? (See also Question 2)

▶ Catching food

The chameleon has a long tongue which it flicks out to catch insects.

The chameleon is also very good at camouflage. It can change colour to match its background.

This owl has special features to help it catch and eat its food (see Question 1).

1 Look at the owl in the photograph (above right). Write down the features you think the owl has to help it:
   a hunt at night.
   b grip small animals.
   c tear small animals apart.
   d keep warm.

2 Look at the photograph on the left.
   The leaf insect looks like a leaf. Explain why this helps it survive.

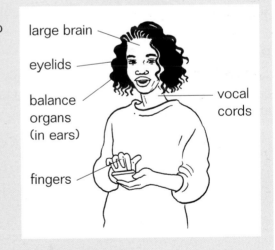

3 Look at the diagram on the right and the sentences below. They are about some of our human features.

The sentences have the wrong endings. Write them out so that the correct parts go together.

We have eyelids...	...to stop us falling over.
We have fingers...	...so that we can speak.
We have a large brain...	...for holding and moving things carefully.
We have balance organs...	...to clear dust from our eyes when we blink.
We have vocal cords...	...so that we can think and remember, and understand our language.

Chains and webs

▶ Food chains

All living things need food. It gives them energy and the
substances they need to build their bodies.

A **food chain** shows how living things feed on other living
things. In the food chain below, the blackbird feeds on the snail,
and the snail feeds on the leaf:

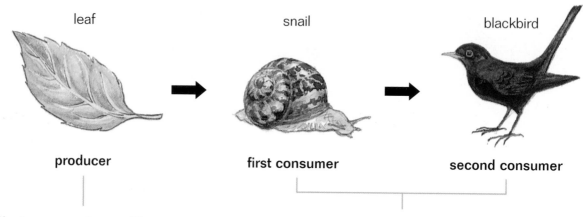

| leaf | snail | blackbird |

| producer | first consumer | second consumer |

Plants are **producers**. They
produce (make) their own food.

Animals are **consumers**. They get their food
by consuming (eating) other living things.

▶ Predators and prey

Animals which kill and eat other animals are
called **predators**. The animals they kill and eat
are their **prey**.

Here are some examples:

predator

prey

Predator	Prey
blackbird	worms insects snails
lion	zebra antelope wildebeest
wolf	reindeer moose
fox	rabbits mice birds

Food webs

Many animals eat more than one type of food. So living things can be part of several food chains. The result is a **food web**. Here is an example:

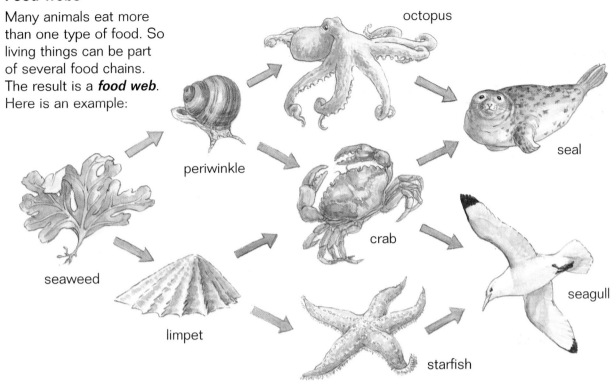

octopus

periwinkle

seaweed

limpet

crab

starfish

seal

seagull

Pollution problems

If poisonous chemicals get into a food chain or web, they can kill lots of living things.

Look at the food web above. If poisonous chemicals are dumped at sea, they may be sucked in by *limpets*. So they will end up in the bodies of all these animals:

crabs   starfish   seals   seagulls

1

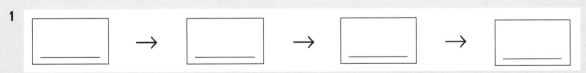

The diagram above shows a food chain. There is some information about the things in it on the right:
Copy the food chain. Fill in the blanks with these words:

caterpillar   thrush   cabbage   fox

> fox feeds on thrush
> caterpillar feeds on cabbage
> thrush feeds on caterpillar

2 Copy and complete these sentences.

In the food chain I have drawn, the producer is....
In the food chain I have drawn, the consumers are....

3 Look at the food web at the top of the page. If *periwinkles* are poisoned by chemicals, what other animals will also get poison in their bodies? Make a list of them.

Looking at matter

▶ Mass

Mass is the amount of matter in something.
It can be measured in *kilograms (kg)*.

Small masses are measured in *grams (g)*.

1000 grams = 1 kilogram

To find the mass of something, you can weigh it.

mass = 53.2 g

53.2 g

▶ Volume

Volume is the amount of space something takes
up. It can be measured in *cubic metres (m³)*.

Small volumes are measured in *millilitres (ml)*,
also called *cubic centimetres (cm³)*.

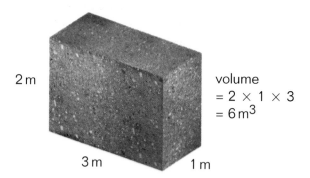

2 m

3 m   1 m

volume
= 2 × 1 × 3
= 6 m³

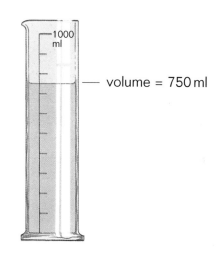

1000 ml

volume = 750 ml

You can work out the volume of a block like this:

volume = length × width × height

You can find the volume of a liquid
using a measuring cylinder.

▶ Density

Steel has a higher *density* than water – it has more kilograms in
every cubic metre.

Density is measured in *kilograms per cubic metre (kg/m³)*:

Densities

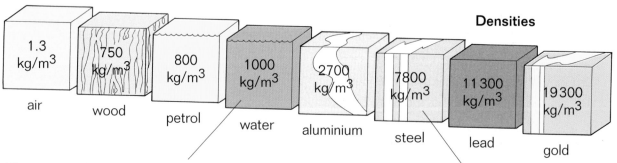

1.3 kg/m³	750 kg/m³	800 kg/m³	1000 kg/m³	2700 kg/m³	7800 kg/m³	11 300 kg/m³	19 300 kg/m³
air	wood	petrol	water	aluminium	steel	lead	gold

This means that there are 1000 kilograms
in every cubic metre of water.

This means that there are 7800 kilograms
in every cubic metre of steel.

Solid, liquid, or gas

Materials can be solid, liquid, or gas. These are their features:

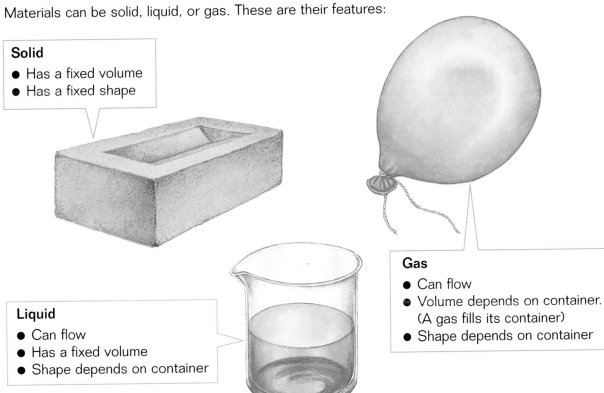

Solid
- Has a fixed volume
- Has a fixed shape

Gas
- Can flow
- Volume depends on container. (A gas fills its container)
- Shape depends on container

Liquid
- Can flow
- Has a fixed volume
- Shape depends on container

Solids, liquids, and gases all have mass.
Gases are usually much lighter than liquids or solids.

1 Copy the table on the right. Put a tick (✓) or a cross (✗) in each box to show the different features of a solid, liquid, and gas.
For example, if you think a solid has a fixed volume, give that box a tick (✓). If you think a solid can't flow, give that box a cross (✗).

Feature ▼	Solid	Liquid	Gas
fixed shape			
fixed volume			
can flow			

2 Look at the density diagram on the left.
Write down the name (or names) of:
a a liquid that is less dense than water.
b two solids that are more dense than steel.
c a gas with a low density.
d a liquid which would have a mass of 2000 kg if you had 2 cubic metres of it.

3   *1   2   100   200   1000   2000*
Copy the following. Fill in the blanks, choosing from the numbers above.
a 1 kg = _____ g
b 2000 g = _____ kg

49

Hot and cold

▶ Changing state

Water can be a solid (ice), a liquid, or a gas (steam):

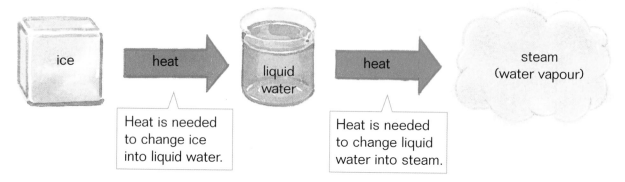

ice | heat | liquid water | heat | steam (water vapour)

Heat is needed to change ice into liquid water.

Heat is needed to change liquid water into steam.

A change from solid to liquid, liquid to gas, or back again is called a change of **state**.

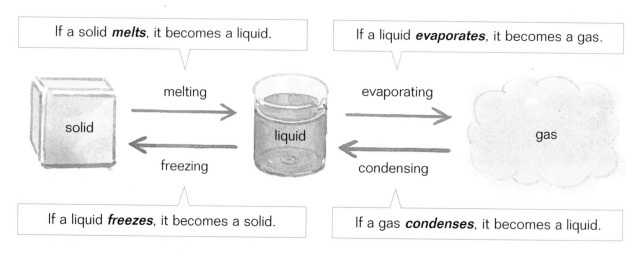

If a solid **melts**, it becomes a liquid.

If a liquid **evaporates**, it becomes a gas.

melting
solid → liquid → evaporating → gas
freezing ← liquid ← condensing

If a liquid **freezes**, it becomes a solid.

If a gas **condenses**, it becomes a liquid.

When water is cold, it evaporates very slowly.

When water is **boiling**, it bubbles, and evaporates very quickly.

The white cloud coming out of a kettle is steam which has condensed to form millions of tiny droplets. The real steam is invisible.

Temperature

When something gets hotter, its *temperature* rises.

Temperature can be measured in **degrees Celsius** *(°C)* (sometimes called 'degrees centigrade').

On the Celsius scale, the numbers were specially chosen so that water freezes at 0 °C and boils at 100 °C.

Temperatures colder than freezing water are given minus numbers. For example, the temperature inside a freezer might be −18 °C.

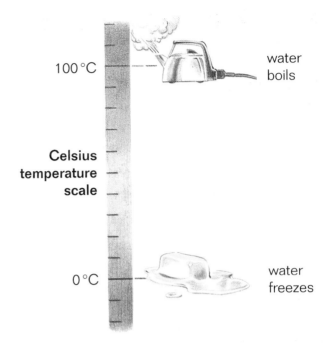

100 °C — water boils

Celsius temperature scale

0 °C — water freezes

Melting and boiling points

The temperature at which a solid melts is called its **melting point**. For example, water has a melting point of 0 °C. This is the temperature at which solid water (ice) changes back to a liquid if you warm it up.

The temperature at which a liquid boils is called its **boiling point**. For example, water has a boiling point of 100 °C.

There are some examples of melting points and boiling points on the right.

Substance	Melting point in °C	Boiling point in °C
hydrogen	−259	−253
oxygen	−219	−183
methane	−183	−162
mercury	−39	357
water	0	100
aluminium	660	2350
iron	1540	2760
tungsten	3387	5420

1 Copy these sentences. Fill in the blanks using the words on the right. (You can use the same word more than once):
   If a solid melts, it becomes a ____.
   If a liquid evaporates, it becomes a ____.
   If a liquid freezes, it becomes a ____.
   If a gas condenses, it becomes a ____.

solid

liquid

gas

2 There are eight substances in the table above. Write down which ones you would expect to be
   a liquid, in a cold room at 5 °C.
   b liquid, in a furnace at 2000 °C.

Particles of matter

▶ **Solids, liquids, and gases**

Solids, liquids, and gases are made up of tiny, moving particles.
These particles attract each other.

Solid
The particles are very close together. They vibrate, but cannot change positions because the attractions are too strong.

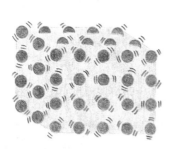

A solid has a fixed volume and a fixed shape.

Reason The particles are very close together and can't change positions

Liquid
The particles are close together. They vibrate, but can change positions because the attractions are not so strong.

A liquid has a fixed volume, but can flow and change shape.

Reason The particles are close together, but can change positions.

Gas
The particles are spaced out. They can move about freely at high speed because the attractions are very weak.

A gas fills its container, and can be compressed

Reason The particles can move about, and are spaced out.

In some substances the particles are atoms. In others they are groups of atoms, called *molecules* (see Spread 3.04).

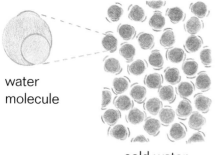

water molecule

cold water   hot water

When the temperature of water rises, the molecules vibrate faster.

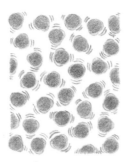

water vapour (steam)

When the molecules are vibrating fast enough, they break free from each other and form a gas (see Spread 3.02).

▶ Spreading particles: diffusion

Smells spread quickly across a room. This is why it happens:

Smells are gas particles coming from food, or perfume, or anything smelly. These particles spread through the air as particles in the air keep bumping into them. The spreading of particles like this is called **diffusion**.

The photograph on the right shows another example of diffusion. The trifle has been left for a couple of days. The colours have spread across the top by diffusion.

▶ Gas pressure

When you blow up a balloon, its sides are pushed out by the **pressure** of the gas inside. This is what causes the pressure:

Inside the balloon, there are millions of gas particles. As they move about at high speed, they keep hitting the inside of the balloon. Each collision produces a tiny force. Together, millions of collisions push out the sides.

---

1 *material   gas   liquid   solid*

Copy the sentences below. Fill in the blanks, choosing words from those above.

a In a _____ , the particles are spaced out and move about at high speed.

b In a _____ , the particles are close together and cannot change positions.

c In a _____ , the particles are close together and can change positions.

2 Using your ideas about particles, copy and complete these sentences:

The smell of perfume spreads across a room because.....

There is pressure inside a balloon because.....

Elements, atoms, and compounds

▶ Elements

Everything on Earth is made from about 90 simple substances called *elements*.

There are two main types of element: *metals* and *nonmetals*. Here are some examples, with their chemical symbols:

Metals	
Element	*Symbol*
aluminium	Al
calcium	Ca
copper	Cu
gold	Au
iron	Fe
lead	Pb
magnesium	Mg
potassium	K
silver	Ag
sodium	Na
tin	Sn
zinc	Zn

Nonmetals	
Element	*Symbol*
bromine	Br
carbon	C
chlorine	Cl
fluorine	F
helium	He
hydrogen	H
iodine	I
nitrogen	N
oxygen	O
phosphorus	P
silicon	Si
sulphur	S

Metals are usually hard, shiny, and difficult to melt. They are good conductors of heat and electricity. (For more on metals, see Spread 3.10.)

Examples

Copper

Aluminium

Nonmetals are usually gases, or solids which melt easily. The solids are often brittle or powdery. Most nonmetals are insulators – though carbon is a good conductor of electricity.

Examples

 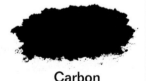

Sulphur   **Carbon**

▶ Atoms

atoms in a bar of copper

The smallest bit of an element is called an *atom*. Each element has its own type of atom.

Atoms are very, very small. It would take more than a billion billion atoms to cover this dot!

▶ Compounds

Atoms can join together to form new substances, called **compounds**. These may be nothing like the elements in them.

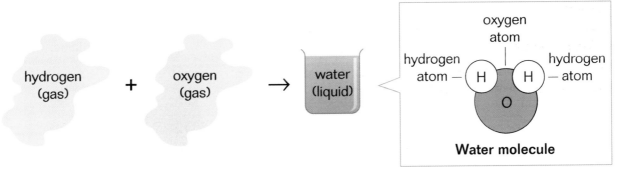

Water is a compound of hydrogen and oxygen. It is made when hydrogen burns in oxygen. But it is nothing like either of these.

The smallest bit of water is called a **molecule** of water. It is made of two hydrogen atoms stuck to one oxygen atom.

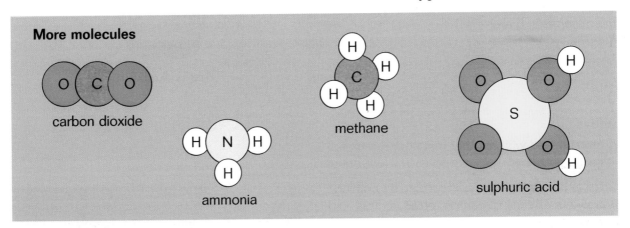

Atoms don't really have colours. The colours here are to help you tell the atoms apart.

1 nonmetals   metals   atoms   compounds   elements

Copy these sentences. Fill in the blanks, choosing words from those above. You can use the same word more than once.

_____ are usually hard and shiny.
_____ are the smallest bits of elements.
_____ are good conductors of heat and electricity.
_____ are usually insulators.
_____ are made from more than one element.

2 Write down the names of the elements with these symbols:
   H   O   C   N   S

3 Copy the table on the right. Fill in the blanks by writing in the elements in each compound. The first one has been done for you.

Compound	Elements
ammonia	nitrogen hydrogen
water	
carbon dioxide	
sulphuric acid	

Mixtures and solutions

▶ Mixtures

One substance by itself is called a *pure* substance.

Most substances are not like this. They have other things mixed in. They are *mixtures*.

Mineral water may not be pure, but this does not mean it is dirty. Many of the minerals in it are good for you.

Distilled water
Contains: water

This is pure

Mineral water
Contains: water

+ small amounts of
   bicarbonates
   calcium
   chlorides
   sodium
   magnesium
   potassium
   silica
   sulphates
   nitrates

This is a mixture

▶ Alloys

A metal mixed with another metal (or nonmetal) is called an *alloy*.

Steel is an alloy of iron and carbon. It is mainly iron with a little bit of carbon mixed in. This makes it harder and stronger than iron by itself.

Steel
iron
+ carbon

Brass
copper
+ zinc

Stainless steel
iron
+ chromium
+ carbon

Bronze
copper
+ tin

Brass is an alloy of copper and zinc. Unlike pure copper, it keeps its shine and colour.

▶ Solutions

If you put sugar in water, the sugar breaks up into tiny bits which float away. The bits are so small that you cannot see them even with a microscope.

The sugar has **dissolved** in the water.
Scientists say that sugar is **soluble** in water.
The mixture of sugar and water is called a **solution**:

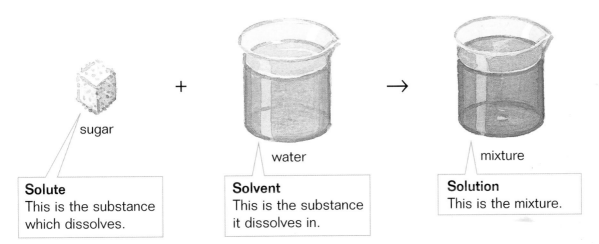

sugar   water   mixture

Solute
This is the substance which dissolves.

Solvent
This is the substance it dissolves in.

Solution
This is the mixture.

Water is not the only solvent. Here are some others:

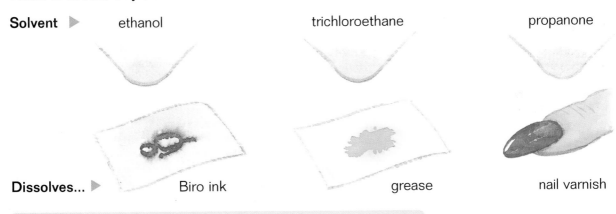

Solvent ▶   ethanol   trichloroethane   propanone

Dissolves... ▶   Biro ink   grease   nail varnish

---

1 *solution   alloy   pure substance*
Write down which of the things above means each of these:
a One substance by itself
b A metal mixed with another metal (or nonmetal).

2 *solvent   solute   dissolves   soluble   solution*
Copy these sentences. Fill in the blanks, choosing words from those above.
When salt is mixed with water, the salt ____ in the water.
Salt is ____ in water.
The water is called the ____.
The mixture is called a ____.

For more about water as a solvent, see Spread 3.12

Separating mixtures

Here are some methods of separating mixtures in the laboratory:

Filtering

Example Separating sand from water.

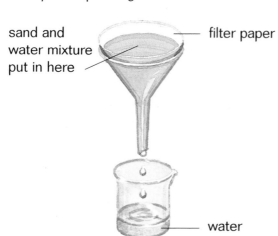

sand and water mixture put in here — filter paper

water

Pour the mixture into a funnel lined with filter paper. The filter paper lets the water through but stops the sand.

Dissolving and filtering

Example Separating sand from salt.

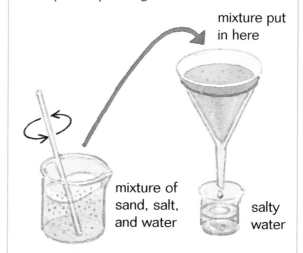

mixture put in here

mixture of sand, salt, and water

salty water

Mix the sand and salt with water, and stir. This dissolves the salt, but not the sand. Filter the new mixture. The filter paper lets the salty water through but stops the sand.

Evaporating

Example Separating salt from water.

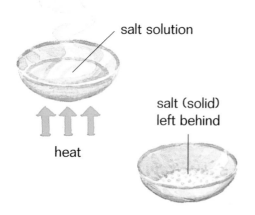

salt solution

salt (solid) left behind

heat

Heat the solution gently until all the water has evaporated. The salt is left behind as a solid.

Distilling

Example Separating water from ink.

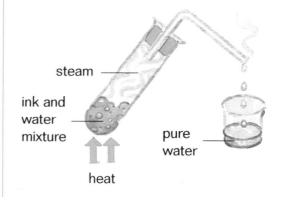

steam

ink and water mixture

pure water

heat

Boil the mixture so that it gives off steam. The steam is pure water vapour, with no ink in it. As the steam passes down the tube, it condenses into pure, liquid water.

Crystallizing

Example Separating copper sulphate from water.

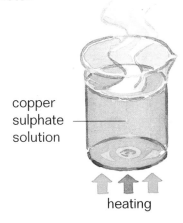

copper sulphate solution

heating

Heat the solution gently, so that some of the water evaporates.

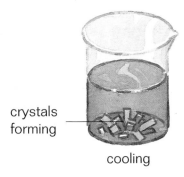

crystals forming

cooling

Leave the rest of the solution to cool. Copper sulphate crystals will start to form in it.

Chromatography

Example Separating inks of different colours.

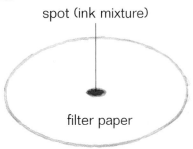

spot (ink mixture)

filter paper

Put a spot of ink mixture in the middle of a piece of filter paper and leave it to dry.

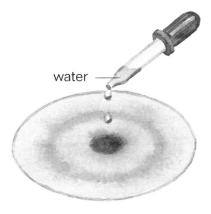

water

Drip water onto the spot. The ink mixture spreads through the damp paper. The different colours spread at different rates.

---

1 Here are some methods of separating mixtures:
*filtering   evaporating   crystallizing   distilling
dissolving and filtering   chromatography*

Write down which method you would use for each of these jobs (the information on the right may help):
a Separating sand and salt.
b Separating sand and sugar.
c Separating mud and water.
d Separating water paints of different colours.

2 A tea-bag is a filter. Write down what things you think it separates.

3 The bag in a vacuum cleaner is a filter. Write down what things you think it separates.

Mud is tiny bits of soil floating in water

Sugar will dissolve in water

3.07 Acids and alkalis

Acids

There are acids in the laboratory. But there are natural acids in vinegar, sour fruits, and even in your stomach!

Acids dissolved in lots of water are called *dilute* acids. Acids dissolved in only a little water are *concentrated* acids.

When dissolved in water, acids are *corrosive* . They eat into materials such as carbonates and some metals.

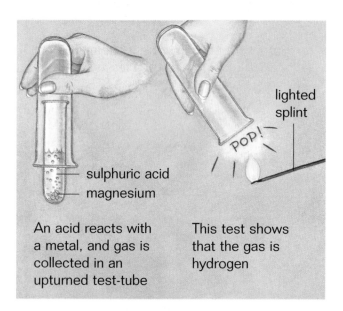

lighted splint

POP!

sulphuric acid
magnesium

An acid reacts with a metal, and gas is collected in an upturned test-tube

This test shows that the gas is hydrogen

Some natural acids

	contains....
lemon juice	citric acid
vinegar	ethanoic acid
fizzy drinks	carbonic acid
sour milk	lactic acid
nettle sting	methanoic acid
stomach juice	hydrochloric acid

Strong acids
hydrochloric acid
sulphuric acid
nitric acid

Weak acids
ethanoic acid
citric acid
carbonic acid

All acids contain hydrogen. When an acid eats into a metal, the hydrogen is released as a gas.

Acids which act quickly, and release lots of hydrogen, are called *strong acids*. Acids which act slowly are *weak acids*.

Alkalis

Alkalis are chemicals which can *neutralize* acids.
They can cancel out their acid effect (see the next page).

Strong alkalis
sodium hydroxide
potassium hydroxide
calcium hydroxide

Weak alkali
ammonia

Alkalis can be just as corrosive as acids. Their powerful chemical action is often used in bath, sink, and oven cleaners, like those in the picture.

▶ Neutralization

Neutralizing acids is called **neutralization**. Here are two examples:

Sugar in your mouth produces acids which rot your teeth. Toothpaste is alkaline. It neutralizes these acids.

Acid in your stomach can become a bit too concentrated. Indigestion tablets release an alkali which neutralizes some of the acid.

▶ Testing for acids and alkalis

You can use **litmus paper** to test for an acid or alkali:

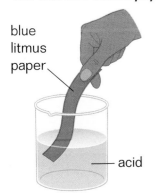
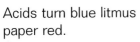

blue litmus paper
— acid

Acids turn blue litmus paper red.

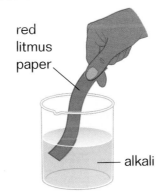

red litmus paper
— alkali

Alkalis turn red litmus paper blue.

If a solution is **neutral** (neither acid nor alkaline), the paper doesn't change colour.

The pH scale

Scientists use the **pH scale** to measure how strong or weak an acid or alkali is. Here are some examples of pH numbers:

	pH
very strong acid	1
weak acid	6
neutral solution*	7
weak alkali	8
very strong alkali	14

* pure water is neutral, and has a pH of 7

---

1 Copy the table on the right. Write 'acid' or 'alkali' in each blank space.

2 Copy and complete these sentences:
  a An acid dissolved in lots of water is called a .... acid.
  b An acid dissolved in only a little water is called a .... acid.
  c If an acid eats into a metal, ... is released.
  d If an alkali *neutralizes* an acid, this means that........
  e A neutral solution has a pH of........

	acid or alkali
Sour milk	acid
Turns blue litmus paper red	
Turns red litmus paper blue	
Lemon juice	
Indigestion tablets	
Vinegar	
pH less than 7	

Changing materials

▶ **Chemical change**

When iron and sulphur are mixed and heated, they join to make a completely new substance, iron sulphide.

 +  $\xrightarrow{\text{heat}}$

iron (metal)   sulphur (yellow powder)   iron sulphide (black solid)

This is an example of a **chemical change**. Iron has **reacted** with sulphur. There has been a **chemical reaction** between the two. Here is a **word equation** for the reaction:

iron + sulphur → iron sulphide

▶ **Signs of chemical change**

If there is a chemical change:

One or more new substances are made
Iron sulphide is a compound (see Spread 3.04). It is nothing like iron or sulphur.

The change is usually difficult to reverse
Changing iron sulphide back into iron and sulphur is difficult. Several reactions are needed.

Energy is given out or taken in
When iron reacts with sulphur, heat is given out.

Here are some examples of chemical change:

Once you have cooked eggs, you can't change them back again.

These chemical reactions give out energy as heat and light.

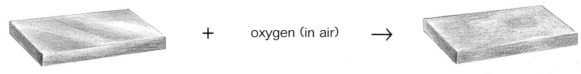

iron	rust (iron oxide)

If there is water around, a chemical change turns these.....   ......into this.

▶ Physical change

If liquid water freezes, it becomes ice. This is an example of a **physical change**. If there is a physical change:

No new substances are made
Ice is still water, even though it is a solid.

The change is usually easy to reverse
Ice can melt to form liquid water again.

Here are some examples of physical change:

Liquid water can change into steam. When steam condenses, it becomes liquid water again.

Salt dissolves in water. But if you evaporate the water, you are left with the salt again.

1 *physical   chemical*

Copy these sentences. Fill in the blanks, choosing words from those above. (You can use the same word more than once.)

a In a ____ change, one or more new substances are made.

b A ____ change is usually difficult to reverse.

c In a ____ change, you end up with the same substance that you started with.

2 Copy the table on the right. Fill in the blanks, by writing 'physical' or 'chemical' in each space. The first one has been done for you.

	Change: physical or chemical
Cooking an egg	chemical
Ice melting	
Salt dissolving in water	
Baking a cake	
Iron going rusty	
Hot fat going solid when cooled	
Wood burning	

Burning

▶ Combustion

Combustion is another word for burning. When things burn, they give out energy as heat and light.

Burning happens when substances react rapidly with oxygen. For example:

When magnesium burns, its atoms join with oxygen atoms from the air to form magnesium oxide. There is a word equation for the reaction below:

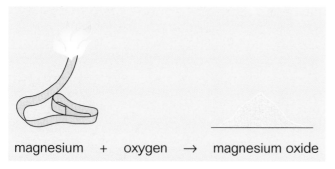

magnesium   +   oxygen   →   magnesium oxide

The magnesium oxide (ash) weighs more than the magnesium because of the added oxygen.

Combustion

▶ Burning fuels

Petrol, coal, wood, and natural gas (methane) are all **fuels**.

Most fuels are compounds of hydrogen and carbon. When they burn, they make carbon dioxide and water, as on the right.

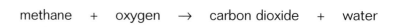

methane   +   oxygen   →   carbon dioxide   +   water

| atoms of: carbon hydrogen | atoms of: oxygen | atoms of: carbon oxygen | atoms of: hydrogen oxygen |

wooden splint

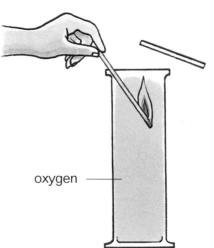

oxygen

Testing for oxygen Fuels burn more fiercely in pure oxygen than in air. You can use this fact to test for oxygen:

If a glowing wooden splint is put into oxygen, the splint will burst into flames.

▶ Fire!

The **combustion triangle** below shows the three things needed for burning. Getting rid of any of them stops the burning. So firefighters have three ways of putting out a fire.

Get rid of the heat
For example Cool things down with water.

Note Water is not safe for some fires. It conducts electricity and can give people shocks. Also, it can make burning fat or oil splatter and spread.

Cut off the air supply
For example Use a fire blanket, foam, or carbon dioxide gas.

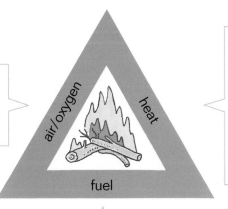

Cut off the fuel
For example Turn off the gas at the mains.

▶ Burning food

To get energy, your body 'burns up' food slowly, without any flames. This is called **respiration** (see Spreads 2.02 and 2.08). It makes carbon dioxide and water:

food + oxygen → carbon dioxide + water

▶ Testing for carbon dioxide

Carbon dioxide turns **limewater** milky. You can use this fact to tell that there is carbon dioxide in the air you breathe out.

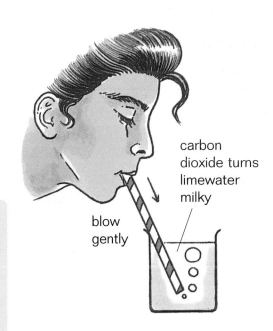

carbon dioxide turns limewater milky

blow gently

1 Here are three gases:
   oxygen   carbon dioxide   methane
   Write down which gas does each of these.
   (You can choose the same gas more than once.)
   a Puts out fires.
   b Is needed for burning.
   c Is made when most fuels burn.
   d Is used as a fuel.
   e Makes a glowing splint burst into flames.
   f Is made when your body 'burns up' food.
   g Turns limewater milky.

2 Write down the *three* things needed for burning.

The burning of fuels causes pollution: see Spreads 2.17 and 4.11

More about metals

▶ Corrosion

The surface of a metal may be attacked by air, water, or other substances around it. This is called **corrosion**. Iron corrodes by going rusty. Steel is mainly iron. It can also go rusty.

The experiment on the right shows that air *and* water are needed for rusting. Dry air has no effect. Nor does water, if it has no air in it.

To stop iron and steel going rusty, they can be coated with paint, grease, plastic, or zinc.

Iron nail in.....

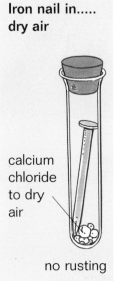
dry air

calcium chloride to dry air

no rusting

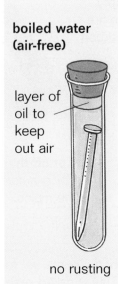
boiled water (air-free)

layer of oil to keep out air

no rusting

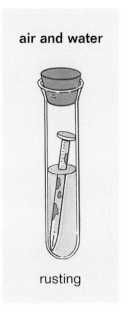
air and water

rusting

▶ Reactive and unreactive

Iron is a **reactive** metal. It reacts with other elements to form compounds. For example, it reacts with oxygen in the air to form rust.

Gold is an **unreactive** metal. It does not react with oxygen or acids. So it does not corrode however long it is left in the air or soil.

▶ Reacting with oxygen

The chart below shows how four different metals react when heated and put in a gas jar containing pure oxygen. If there is a reaction, a compound called an **oxide** is formed.

Metal	Reaction with oxygen	Compound formed
magnesium	burns easily with brilliant white flame	magnesium oxide (white powder)
iron	only burns if in the form of a powder or wire-wool	iron oxide (black powder)
copper	does not burn, but black substance forms on surface	copper oxide (black powder)
gold	no reaction, even with strong heating	–

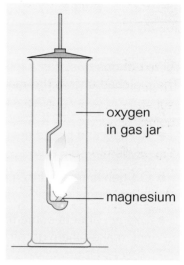

Magnesium reacting with oxygen

▶ Reacting with acid

The chart below shows how the four metals react with an acid. If there is a reaction, *hydrogen* is given off.

Metal	Reaction with acid (dilute hydrochloric)	Gas given off
magnesium	reacts very quickly	hydrogen
iron	reacts slowly	hydrogen
copper	no reaction	–
gold	no reaction	–

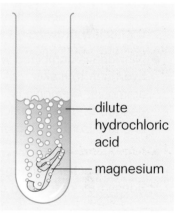

Magnesium reacting with an acid

---

1 Write down *two* things which are needed for iron or steel to go rusty.

2 Write down *two* ways of stopping iron or steel going rusty.

3 *oxide   acid   hydrogen*

Write down the word above which goes with each of these:
a Formed when a metal burns in oxygen
b Given off when a metal reacts with an acid.

4 From the four metals listed on the right, choose one for each of these (you can use the same answer more than once):
a More reactive than the other metals with acid
b More reactive than the other metals with oxygen
c Does not react with acid or oxygen.

> copper
>
> iron
>
> gold
>
> magnesium

3.11 Air

Air is not one gas. It is a mixture of gases.
The pie chart shows the main gases in air.

Oxygen

- Animals and plants need oxygen to stay alive.
- Oxygen is needed to make things burn.
- Oxygen affects some foods and makes them go off.

Carbon dioxide and other gases

- These are just a tiny fraction of the air. There is more about them on the next page.

Nitrogen

- Nitrates have nitrogen in them. Plants need nitrates for healthy growth.
- Nitrogen is combined with hydrogen to make ammonia. Ammonia is needed to make plastics, and fertilizers for farmers.
- Nitrogen helps preserve food in packets. Nitrogen doesn't make food go off.

- Very cold, liquid nitrogen is used for freezing food quickly.

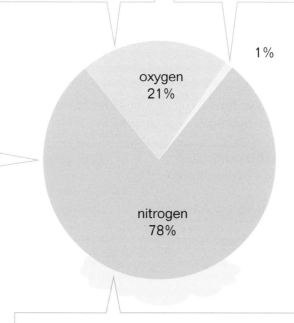

1%

oxygen
21%

nitrogen
78%

Water vapour

- Damp air has some water vapour in it. When water vapour condenses into millions of tiny drops, we see these as clouds and fog.

Carbon dioxide....

- Plants take in carbon dioxide for growth.

- Some fire extinguishers shoot out carbon dioxide. Things can't burn in carbon dioxide.

- Carbon dioxide is the gas that puts the fizz in fizzy drinks.

- Solid carbon dioxide is called 'dry ice'. It is much colder than ordinary ice. It is used for storing frozen fish and other foods.

...and other gases

- Argon is used to fill light bulbs. It stops the filament burning up.

- Helium is lighter than other gases in air. It is used to fill balloons.

- Neon is used in lamps that give a red glow.

1 On the right, there are the names of four gases:
Write down the gas that goes with each of these clues.
(You can choose the same gas more than once.)
a There is more of this gas in air than any other.
b This gas is needed for things to burn.
c When this gas freezes, it becomes 'dry ice'.
d This gas is needed to make nitrates for plants.

2 Copy and complete these sentences. You must start each sentence with one of the gases on the right, then finish it with your own words:
a _____ is used to fill balloons because.....
b _____ is used in fire extinguishers because.....
c _____ is used to fill crisp packets because.....

3 The gases on the right are all part of the air. Write down the name of *one* other gas in air. Describe what it is used for.

carbon dioxide

oxygen

nitrogen

helium

3.12 Water

Here are some facts about water:

- Two-thirds of the Earth's surface is covered with water.
- All living things need water.
- Our bodies are two-thirds water.
- Water can be a solid (ice), a liquid, or a gas (water vapour).
- Water dissolves some substances.

Water as a solvent

Sugar dissolves in water. Water is a *solvent*. The mixture of sugar and water is called a *solution* (see Spread 3.05)

Many other substances will dissolve in water. The table on the right gives some examples. Some of them are gases.

Saturated solutions

If you stir a little bit of sugar into a hot drink, all the crystals will dissolve. But if you add lots more sugar, some will not dissolve. The solution is *saturated*.

The amount of a substance you can dissolve depends on the temperature. For example:

Substance dissolving in water	Description
sodium chloride	Common salt: the salt in sea water
copper sulphate	Blue crystals
calcium carbonate	Chalk, limestone
carbon dioxide	The gas in fizzy drinks
chlorine	The gas used to kill germs in swimming pool water

This mass of copper sulphate...   20 grams   40 grams   75 grams

...will dissolve in 100 grams of water at this temperature   20 °C   60 °C   100 °C

Like copper sulphate, most solids dissolve more easily as the temperature rises.

Gases dissolve less easily as the temperature rises. For example, less carbon dioxide will dissolve in hot water than in cold.

▶ Freezing water

Water freezes at 0 °C.

When water freezes it expands. It takes up more space than before.

The force of the expansion can be huge.

This much water...   ...becomes this much ice

Here are some of the effects of freezing water:

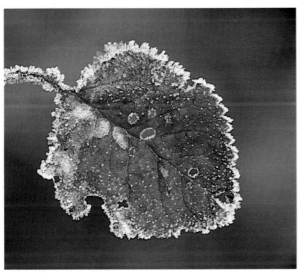

Water vapour condenses on cold ground or plants to form *dew*. When dew freezes, it is called *frost*.

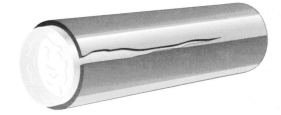

Pipes burst when water in them freezes.

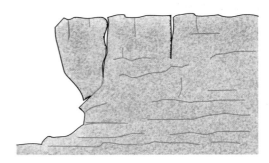

Rocks split when water freezes in cracks.

1 Write down an example of:
   a a solid which will dissolve in water
   b a gas which will dissolve in water.

2 Look at the diagram on the opposite page.
   Leanne is going to mix 40 grams of copper sulphate crystals with 100 grams of water. If the water is at each of these temperatures, will all the crystals dissolve?
   a 50 °C   b 60 °C   c 70 °C
   (Write down YES or NO for each temperature.)

3 Copy and complete these sentences:

   Dew is formed when....
   Frozen dew is called.....
   When water pipes freeze, they burst because.....

Rock, stone, and soil

▶ Weathering

If rock or stonework is exposed (out in the open), it is weakened by the weather. This is called **weathering**.

The effects of weathering on stonework.

Sunshine heats some parts more than others. The expansion cracks the rock.

Rock splits when water freezes in cracks.

Rain is slightly acid. It eats into some rocks, such as chalk and limestone.

▶ Soil

Soil is mainly made from the rock underneath it. The rock gets broken up by rain, frost, and expansion caused by the Sun's heat.

Soil is made from the smaller bits of broken rock.

Stones are the bigger bits of broken rock.

Under the soil, there is solid rock.

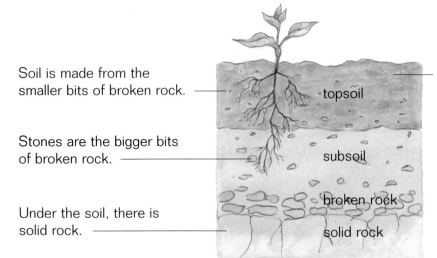

topsoil

subsoil

broken rock

solid rock

Topsoil has rotting plant and animal waste in it. This is called **humus**. It is rich in the minerals that plants need.

The rock cycle

Materials from rocks are used over and over again. This is called the **rock cycle**. It can take millions of years. Here is one part of it:

Weathering
Exposed rock is weakened by the weather.

Erosion
The weak surface is **eroded** (worn away) by wind or water.

New rock
Compressed by the weight above, the bits join to make new rock.

Deposition
The bits are deposited (dropped) as **sediment**, such as mud or sand.

Transport
The bits are carried off by wind or water. Or they just fall.

Weathering

Erosion

Transport

Deposition

sediment

New rock forming

1 *weathering   erosion   humus   sediment*
Choosing from the words above, write down the word which goes with each of these clues.
   a The wearing away of rock or soil.
   b Mud and sand are examples of this.
   c Rotting plant and animal waste in soil.

2 Write out these sentences in the correct order, starting with the one which means 'weathering'.
   Bits of rock are dropped as sediment.
   Bits of compressed rock join together.
   Bits of rock are carried off by wind or water.
   Exposed rock is weakened by the weather.
   Bits of rock are worn away by wind or water.

Looking at rocks

The Earth is made of rock. Deep in the Earth, the rock is so hot that it is *molten* (melted). Sometimes, molten rock comes out of volcanoes, as in the photograph.

The Earth's surface changes slowly over millions of years. Rocks in the ground may be raised up and exposed. Other rocks may be buried.

There are three main types of rocks:

▶ **Igneous rocks**

These are made of tiny crystals. They are formed when molten rock cools and goes solid.

Examples

Granite This went solid underground. It was exposed when rocks above it were worn away.

Basalt This formed from molten rock which oozed out of cracks in the Earth.

▶ **Sedimentary rocks**

These are made from layers of sediment dropped by water, wind, or moving ice. The sediment is compressed by the weight above and sets like concrete. But this takes millions of years.

Examples

Sandstone This formed from bits worn away from other rocks.

Limestone This formed from the shells and bones of ancient sea creatures.

Metamorphic rocks

Deep underground, igneous and sedimentary rocks can be changed by heat or pressure. They become *metamorphic* ('changed') rocks.

Examples

Marble This formed from *limestone* when it was heated underground.

Slate This formed from *shale (mudstone)* when it was compressed underground.

Using rocks

We get minerals, such as diamond and gold, from rocks. The word 'mineral' really means anything useful that can be mined from the Earth.

The table shows some more uses of rocks.

Rock	Description	Examples of use
Granite	Very hard, sparkling	chippings,road stone building stone
Limestone	light colour	building/facing stone chippings in cement, concrete
Marble	light colour, hard,smooth	facing stone statues
Slate	hard, but splits into flat sheets	roofing tiles snooker tables

1 *igneous   sedimentary   metamorphic*

Copy these sentences. Fill in the blanks using the words above.

a Rocks formed from bits of rock or shell, dropped in layers, are called ____ rocks.

b Rocks formed when molten rock cools and goes solid are called ____ rocks.

c Rocks changed by heat or pressure are called ____ rocks.

2 Copy the table on the right. Fill in the blanks by giving one example of each type of rock and one use for that rock. (The name of one rock has been written in for you.)

Rock	Used for
igneous: granite	
sedimentary:	
metamorphic:	

Electricity in action

'Electricity' is another word for **electric charge**.
The photograph shows electric charge in action.

▶ Charges from the atom

Electric charge comes from atoms. There are two types of charge. These are called **positive** (+) and **negative** (−).

An atom has equal amounts of negative (−) and positive (+) charge. So the charges balance.

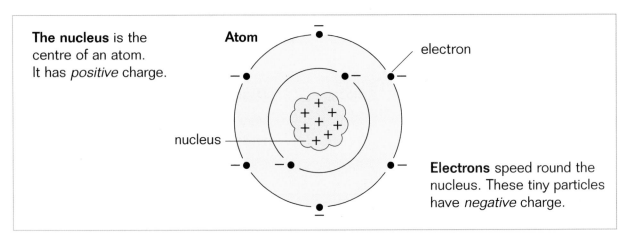

The nucleus is the centre of an atom. It has *positive* charge.

Atom

electron

nucleus

Electrons speed round the nucleus. These tiny particles have *negative* charge.

▶ Conductors and insulators

Electrons do not always stay with atoms. When you switch on a light, electrons flow through the wires by passing between the atoms. A flow of electrons is called a **current**.

Conductors let electrons flow through.

Conductors	
Good	*Poor*
metals,	human body
especially	water
silver	air
copper	
aluminium	
carbon	

Insulators do not let electrons flow through.

Insulators	
plastics	glass
for example	rubber
PVC	
polythene	
Perspex	

▶ Sources of electricity

Here are some of the things that can push electrons through wires:

Batteries have chemicals in them. When the chemicals react with each other, this makes electrons move.

This computer game is powered by batteries

Generators have magnets and coils of wire inside them. Turning the magnets makes electrons move through the coils.

Mains electricity comes from huge generators in power stations. (For more about power stations, see Spread 4.11.) Car engines have generators to keep the battery charged up.

Solar cells have materials in them which use the energy in sunlight to make electrons move.

Some calculators are powered by solar cells. Some satellites have huge panels of solar cells to produce the electricity they need.

This calculator is powered by solar cells.

---

1 *insulator   conductor   current*
   Choose the word above which goes with each of these:
   a A flow of electrons
   b This will not let current pass through it.

2 Copy the table on the right.
   The tick shows that air is a poor conductor of electricity. Put in more ticks to complete the table.

3 Write down
   a *Three* things powered by batteries
   b *Two* things powered by generators
   c *One* thing powered by solar cells.

Material	Good conductor	Poor conductor	Insulator
air		✓	
copper			
glass			
plastic			
aluminium			
carbon			
water			

4.02 A simple circuit

This is called a *circuit*. The **battery** has two **terminals**. It pushes electrons out of the negative (−) terminal, round the circuit, to the positive (+) terminal.

When electrons pass through the bulb, they heat up a *filament* (thin wire) so that it glows.

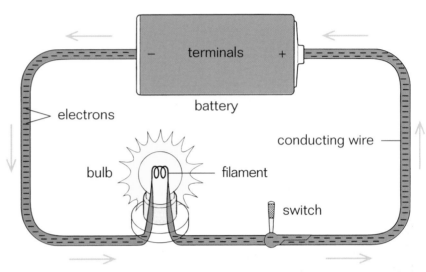

There must be a *complete* circuit for electrons to flow. If there is a break in the circuit, the flow stops, and the bulb goes out. Turning the switch OFF breaks the circuit.

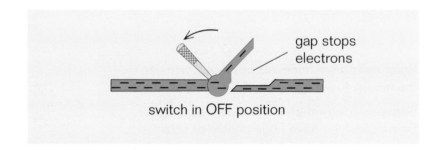

switch in OFF position

gap stops electrons

▶ **Spending energy**

The battery *gives* electrons energy. The electrons *spend* this energy when they flow through the bulb. The bulb sends out energy as heat and light.

For more on energy, see Spread 4.09.

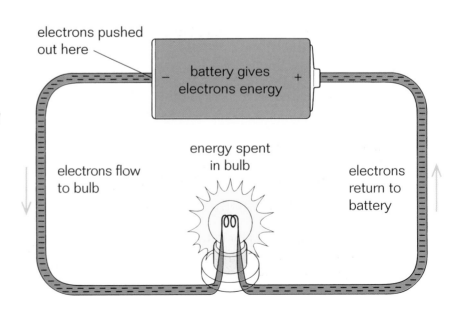

▶ Voltage

A battery has a **voltage** marked on the side. It is measured in **volts (V)**. A higher voltage means that each electron has more energy to spend.

To measure the voltage of a battery, you connect a **voltmeter** across its terminals.

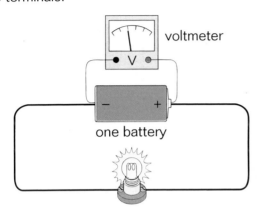

one battery

1.5 volt battery

▶ Current

Current is measured in **amperes (A)**. A higher current means a bigger flow of electrons.

To measure current, you connect an **ammeter** into the circuit.

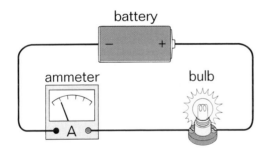

battery

ammeter   bulb

The ammeter can be put anywhere in this circuit, because the current is the same all the way round.

Putting in the ammeter doesn't affect the current.

1 *current   voltage   ammeter   voltmeter*

Copy these sentences. Fill in the blanks, choosing words from those above. (You can use the same word more than once.)

Current is measured with a meter called an ____.
____ is measured in amperes.
If there is a break in a circuit, there is no ____.

2 Copy and complete these statements about the circuit on the right:

Meter Y is called a ......
Meter X is called a ......
The reading on meter X is ......

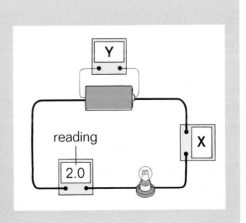

reading

4.03 Batteries and bulbs

▶ **Adding batteries**

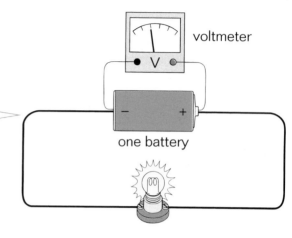

This circuit has one battery in it. The voltmeter is measuring the voltage across the battery.

A single battery is sometimes called a *cell*.

voltmeter

one battery

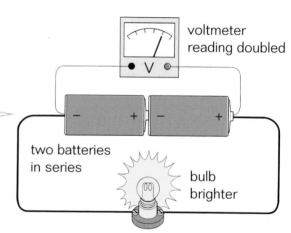

If *two* batteries are put in the circuit like this, the total voltage is twice what it was before. Also, the bulb glows more brightly because a higher current is being pushed through it.

When batteries are connected in a line like this, they are in *series*.

voltmeter reading doubled

two batteries in series

bulb brighter

▶ **Circuit symbols**

Scientists and electricians draw circuits using *symbols*.

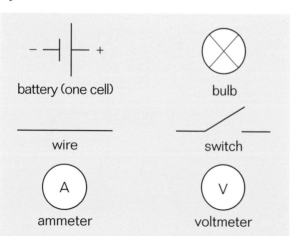

– ⊣⊢ +

battery (one cell)

bulb

wire

switch

A

ammeter

V

voltmeter

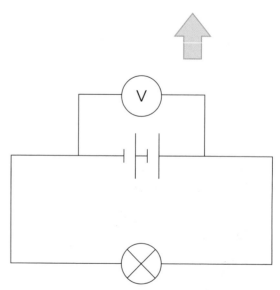

The second circuit, drawn using symbols.

▶ Bulbs in series

This circuit has two bulbs in it. The bulbs are connected in *series* (in a line):

The bulbs glow dimly. It is more difficult for the electrons to pass through two bulbs than one, so there is less current than before.

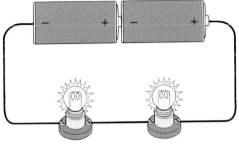

bulbs in series

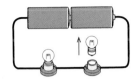

If one bulb is removed, the circuit is broken. So the other bulb goes off.

▶ Bulbs in parallel

This circuit also has two bulbs in it. The bulbs are connected in *parallel*.

The bulbs glow brightly because each is getting the full battery voltage.

Together, two bright bulbs take more current than a single bright bulb, so the battery will not last as long.

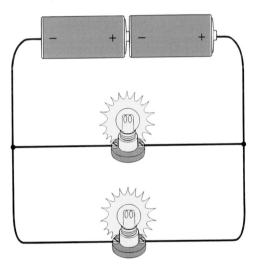

bulbs in parallel

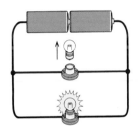

If one bulb is removed, there is still a complete circuit through the other bulb, so it stays bright.

1 Look at the circuit A and B on the right.
  a Write down which circuit, A or B, has the brighter bulb.
  b Explain why this bulb is the brighter.

2 Look at the circuits C and D on the right.
  a Write down which circuit, C or D, has two bulbs in series.
  b Write down which circuit, C or D, has the brighter bulbs.
  c Write down what will happen to bulb 1 if bulb 2 is removed.
  d Write down what will happen to bulb 3 if bulb 4 is removed.

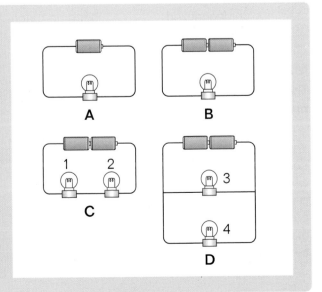

Magnets and electromagnets

▶ Magnets

A few metals are *magnetic*. They are attracted to magnets and can be magnetized. Iron and steel are the main magnetic metals.

The force from a magnet seems to come from two points near the ends. These are the **north pole** (**N**) and the **south pole** (**S**) of the magnet.

When the poles of a magnet are brought close, you can feel the force between them:

Magnetic	Non-magnetic
iron	aluminium
steel*	copper
nickel	brass
	tin
* apart from stainless steel	silver
	gold

magnet (steel)

Like poles repel

 N  **N** **S** **N**

Unlike poles attract

▶ Magnetizing iron and steel

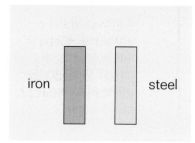

These pieces of iron and steel are unmagnetized.

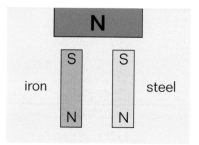

When a magnet is near, they become magnetized.

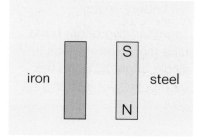

The magnet is taken away. Iron loses its magnetism. Steel keeps its magnetism.

▶ Magnetic fields

The space around a magnet is called a *magnetic field*. The field pulls on anything magnetic.

You can use a **compass** to see which way the field is pulling. A compass is a tiny magnet which can turn on a spindle.

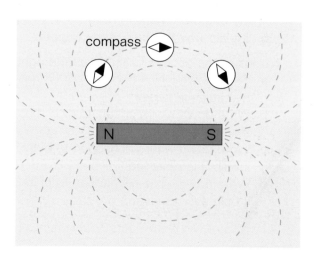

Electromagnet

An electric current produces a magnetic field. This idea is used in an **electromagnet**.

The current in the coil produces a field. The field magnetizes the iron **core**. This makes the field much stronger.

When the electromagnet is switched off, the iron core loses its magnetism and the field vanishes.

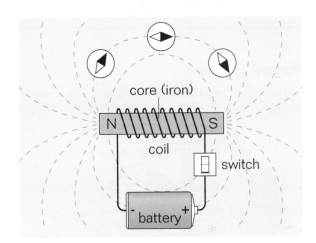

Relay

A **relay** is a switch worked by an electromagnet. With a relay, you can use a tiny switch to turn on a big electric motor powered by mains electricity. The relay works like this:

When you switch on the current in the input circuit, the electromagnet pulls on an iron lever.

When the iron lever is pulled down, it closes two contacts in the output circuit.

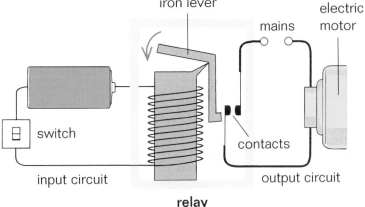

relay

1 *north   south*

Copy these sentences about magnets. Fill in each blank with one of the words above. (You can use the same word more than once.)

A north pole will attract a ____ pole.
A north pole will repel a ____ pole.
A south pole will repel a ____ pole.

2 Copy the table on the right. For each metal, put in a tick to show whether it is *magnetic* or *non-magnetic*. The first one has been done for you.

3 Write down the name of a metal which:
a keeps its magnetism when magnetized.
b loses its magnetism easily.
c can be used as the core of an electromagnet.

Metal	Magnetic	Non-magnetic
nickel	✓	
iron		
aluminium		
copper		
steel		

Forces

► Forces in action

A force is a push or pull. Here are some examples of forces:

Friction This gives a tyre grip on the road when the brakes go on. There is more about friction in Spread 4.08.

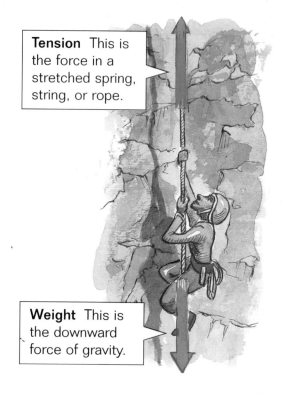

Tension This is the force in a stretched spring, string, or rope.

Weight This is the downward force of gravity.

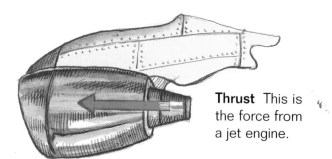

Thrust This is the force from a jet engine.

Air resistance This force tries to slow you down when you are cycling along.

Newtonmeter

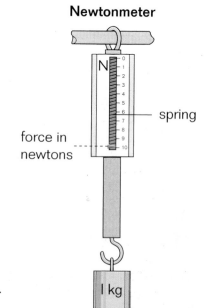

spring

force in newtons

► Measuring force

Force is measured in **newtons (N)**.

Weight is a force. So scientists measure it in newtons, just like any other force.

On Earth, a mass of 1 kilogram has a weight of about 10 newtons. The force can be measured using a **newtonmeter**.

▶ Balanced and unbalanced forces

A skydiver jumps from a helicopter. The forces on her are *air resistance* (upwards) and her *weight* (downwards)......

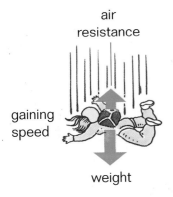

At first, the downward force is stronger than the upward force. The forces are **unbalanced**, so the skydiver **accelerates** (gains speed).

Now, the forces are equal. They are **balanced**. Neither force wins, so she doesn't speed up, and she doesn't slow down. Her speed is *steady*.

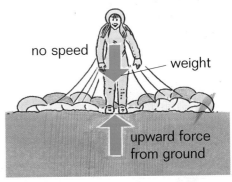

Now she is standing on the ground. The ground is compressed. It pushes upwards and supports her weight. The forces are *balanced*.

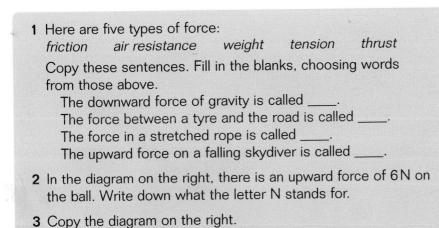

1 Here are five types of force:
   friction   air resistance   weight   tension   thrust
   Copy these sentences. Fill in the blanks, choosing words from those above.
      The downward force of gravity is called ____.
      The force between a tyre and the road is called ____.
      The force in a stretched rope is called ____.
      The upward force on a falling skydiver is called ____.

2 In the diagram on the right, there is an upward force of 6 N on the ball. Write down what the letter N stands for.

3 Copy the diagram on the right.
   Draw in a force arrow for the weight of the ball.
   Next to this force arrow, write down the size of the force (for example 1 N or 2 N or some other value – you must decide).

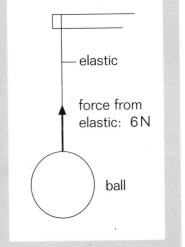

4.06 Pressure

You can't push your thumb into wood. But you *can* push a drawing pin in using the same force. That is because the force is concentrated on a much smaller area. Scientists say that the **pressure** is higher.

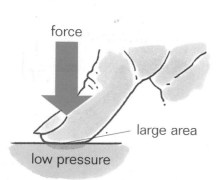

force
large area
low pressure

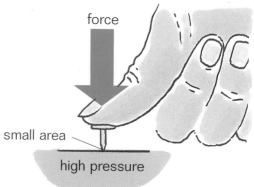

force
small area
high pressure

Spreading the force over a *large area* gives...

low pressure

This ski spreads the skier's weight, so the foot doesn't sink into soft snow.

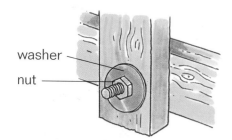

washer
nut

When you tighten the nut, the washer spreads the force, so the nut doesn't go into the wood.

Concentrating the force on a *small area* gives...

high pressure

When the studs on this boot are pressed down, they sink into the ground to give good grip.

A sharp blade concentrates the force so that cutting is easy.

▶ Measuring pressure

Pressure is measured in **newtons per square metre (N/m²)**, also called **Pascals (Pa)**.

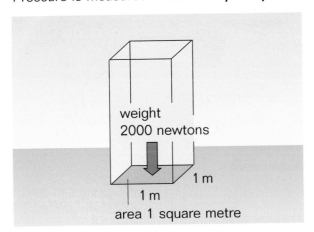

weight
2000 newtons

1 m
1 m
area 1 square metre

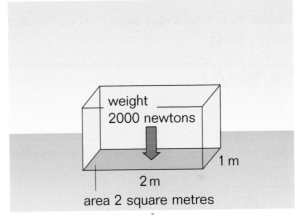

weight
2000 newtons

1 m
2 m
area 2 square metres

This block weighs 2000 newtons. So there is force of 2000 newtons pressing on 1 square metre of ground.

The *pressure* under this block is 2000 newtons per square metre (2000 Pa).

This block also weighs 2000 newtons. But it is pressing on 2 square metres of ground. So there is a force of 1000 newtons on *each square metre*.

The *pressure* under this block is only 1000 newtons per square metre (1000 Pa).

Tyre pressure gauges are sometimes marked in 'psi' (pounds per square inch).

The pressure in this tyre is 50 psi. That is the same as a pressure of 350 000 newtons per square metre (350 000 Pa).

1 Copy these sentences. Write either *high* or *low* in each blank space.
  a If a force is spread over a large area, the pressure is ____.
  b If a force is concentrated on a small area, the pressure is ____.
  c When you push in a drawing pin, the pressure under the point is ____.
  d When you wear skis, the pressure under them is ____.

2 Write down what 'N/m²' means in words.

3 Look at the diagram on the right.
  a Write down how many newtons of force are pressing on *each square metre* of ground.
  b Write down the pressure under the block in N/m².

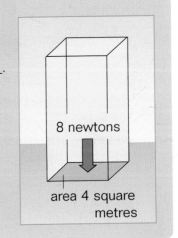

8 newtons

area 4 square metres

4.07 Turning forces

Forces can make things turn. They can have a turning effect.

On the right, someone is using a spanner to turn a bolt. The force has a turning effect on the bolt.

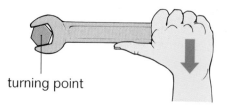

turning point

Here are two ways of making the turning effect *twice* as strong:

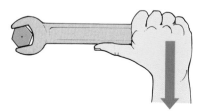

Pull with *twice* the force.

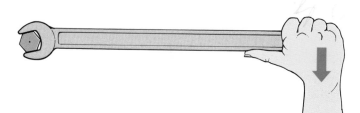

Use a spanner *twice* as long.

▶ **Balance**

The people below are sitting on the see-saw so that it balances.

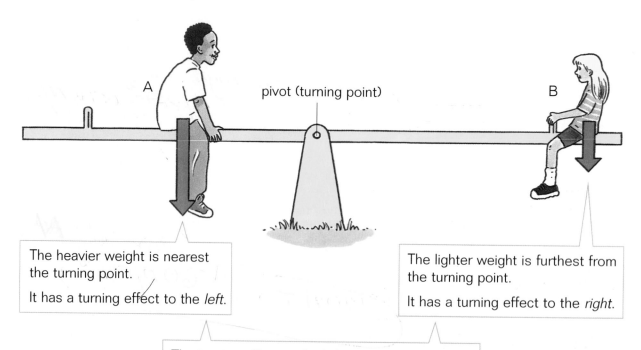

pivot (turning point)

The heavier weight is nearest the turning point.

It has a turning effect to the *left*.

The lighter weight is furthest from the turning point.

It has a turning effect to the *right*.

The turning effect to the left is the *same* as the turning effect to the right. So the plank balances.

▶ Centre of gravity

Every part of your body weighs something. Together, all these tiny forces act like a single force, your **weight**. This is at a point called your **centre of gravity**.

To balance like this, you have to keep your centre of gravity over the beam. Otherwise your weight will have a turning effect and pull you over.

total weight of different parts

=

weight of whole body

centre of gravity

balanced   not balanced

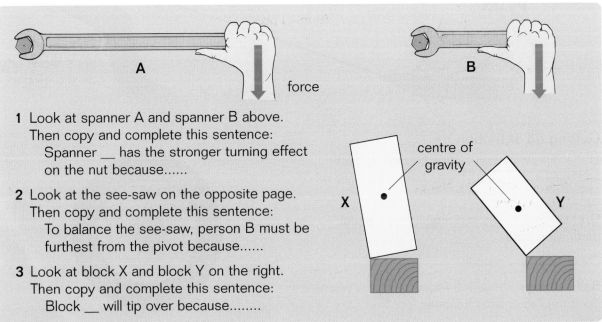

A

force

B

1 Look at spanner A and spanner B above. Then copy and complete this sentence:
   Spanner __ has the stronger turning effect on the nut because......

2 Look at the see-saw on the opposite page. Then copy and complete this sentence:
   To balance the see-saw, person B must be furthest from the pivot because......

3 Look at block X and block Y on the right. Then copy and complete this sentence:
   Block __ will tip over because........

centre of gravity

X   Y

4.08 Moving and stopping

▶ **Speed**

The cyclist in the photograph has a **speed** of.....

15 metres per second

This means that the cyclist will move 15 metres along the track in one second.

Here are some speeds in miles per hour ('mph'), changed into metres per second:

30 mph   70 mph

13 metres per second   31 metres per second

▶ **Friction**

This is the force that tries to stop things sliding past each other.
It can be a problem........   ......but it can be useful.

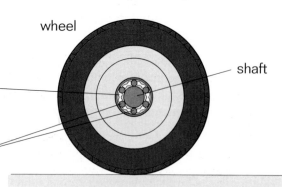

Friction makes it difficult
to drag a sledge over
the ground.

Friction gives
your hands grip
on the rope.

Friction gives
your shoes grip
on the ground.

▶ **Getting rid of friction**

In machinery, friction slows the moving parts and makes them hot. These things help get rid of friction:

wheel

shaft

Grease This is very slippery. It helps metal parts slide easily.

Oil is also very slippery.

Ball bearings These roll round so that a wheel does not rub against its shaft.

Smooth shape

Air resistance is a type of friction. It slows cars down and wastes fuel.

For less air resistance, a car needs a smooth shape so that it slips through the air more easily.

▶ Friction on a bicycle

Friction is a problem:

Air resistance This slows you down. With the wind against you, it slows you even more.

Bearings The wheels spin round on these. Any friction here slows you down.

Friction is useful:

Saddle Friction stops you sliding about.

Handlebar grips Without friction, your hands would slip.

Brakes When rubber blocks press against the wheels, friction slows the wheels down.

Pedals Friction stops your feet slipping.

Tyres Friction lets the tyres grip the road. Without friction, it would be like riding on ice.

---

1 Copy these sentences. Put a word or number in each blank:
   A car has a ___ of 20 metres per second. In 1 second, the car will move ___ metres. In 2 seconds, the car will move ___ metres.

2 Copy the table on the right. Fill in each blank to show whether the friction is *useful* or a *problem*. The first one has been done for you.

3 Look at the cyclist and bicycle in the photograph on the opposite page. Make a list of all the features which help get rid of friction (air resistance is a type of friction).

Example of friction	Friction: *useful* or a *problem*
Walking on ground	useful
Gripping handlebars	
Machinery going round	
Climbing a rope	
Skating on ice	
Putting on brakes	

4.09　Energy

You spend *energy* when you climb the stairs, lift a bag, or hit a ball. Energy is spent whenever a force makes something move.

Some things store energy.

This energy can be used to make other things move.

▶ Forms of energy

Kinetic energy This is the energy of moving things ('kinetic' means 'moving').

Potential energy This is stored energy. You give something potential energy if you lift it up or stretch it.

Chemical energy Foods, fuels, and batteries store energy in this form. Chemical reactions release the energy.

Heat energy (thermal energy) This comes from hot things when they cool down.

Light energy and **sound energy**

Electrical energy This is the energy carried by an electric current.

Nuclear energy This is energy stored in the nucleus of an atom.

► Measuring energy

Energy is measured in **joules (J)**.

50 joules

Energy of a football
when you kick it.

300 000 joules

Energy stored in a
chocolate biscuit.

400 000 000
000 000 000
000 000 000
joules

Energy leaving the Sun
every second.

► Energy chains

When you spend money, it doesn't vanish.
Someone else spends it, then someone
else..... and so on.

When you spend energy, it doesn't vanish. It
changes into a different form, then a different
form..... and so on, in an **energy chain**:

Law of conservation of energy

This law says:

*Energy can change into different forms,
but you cannot make energy and you
cannot destroy it.*

| chemical energy | → | kinetic energy | → | potential energy | → | kinetic energy | → | heat energy |

The body gets this
energy from food.

When things bang or rub
together, they heat up.

---

1 *kilograms   joules   forms*

Copy and complete these sentences, choosing
words from those above.

Energy is measured in ____.
Energy can change into different ____, but it
never vanishes.

2 Copy the table on the right. In each blank space,
write in an example of something with that form
of energy. The first one has been done for you.

Form of energy	Example
light	torch beam
kinetic	
chemical	
potential	

Storing and changing energy

▶ Heat and temperature

A high temperature isn't the same as lots of heat energy:

The sparks from this sparkler are at 1600 °C. But they hold so little heat energy, that they don't burn you when they touch your skin.

This molten (melted) iron is also at 1600 °C. It holds lots of heat energy, and is far too dangerous to touch.

▶ Energy storers

Some things are useful because they store energy:

In this toy, a spring stores energy when you wind it up. When it unwinds, it releases the energy and moves the toy.

This battery stores energy when you connect it to a charger. It delivers the energy as an electric current.

A hot water bottle stores enough energy to keep your feet warm for about an hour.

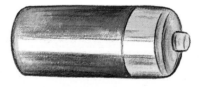

This battery isn't rechargeable. It is made from chemicals which already store energy.

▶ Storing the Sun's energy

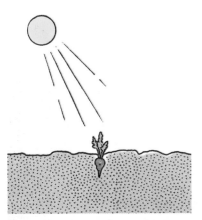

Plants take in energy from sunlight (see Spread 2.02).

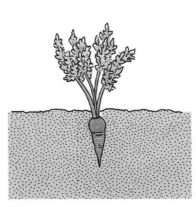

The energy is stored in roots and leaves as they grow.

Animals (like us) can get this energy by eating plants.

▶ Energy changers

Some things are useful because they change energy into a different form:

An electric kettle changes......electrical energy...  ...into heat energy.

A loudspeaker changes..........electrical energy...  ...into sound energy.

A gas ring changes................chemical energy...  ...into heat energy.

---

1 Copy these sentences. Write TRUE or FALSE after each one:
   A kettleful of boiling water has the same temperature as a cupful of boiling water, but it holds more heat energy.
   If something has a high temperature, it must have lots of heat energy.

2 *hairdrier   plant   candle   hot water bottle*

   Copy and complete these sentences, choosing words from those above.
   A ____ stores heat energy.
   A ____ stores energy from the Sun.
   A ____ changes electrical energy into heat energy.
   A ____ changes chemical energy into heat energy.

4.11 Energy for electricity

Our homes and factories need energy. Much of it is supplied by electricity. The electricity comes from **power stations**.

In a power station, the electric power is produced by a **generator**:

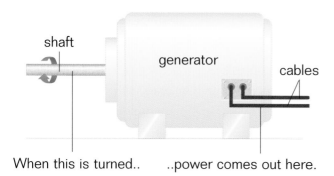

When this is turned.. ..power comes out here.

Turbine

▶ **Inside a power station**

Most large power stations work like this:

The fuel burns here. The fuel is usually coal, oil, or natural gas.

In the boiler, the heat turns water into high pressure steam.

The turbines are blown round by jets of steam.

The turbines turn a generator. This produces the electricity.

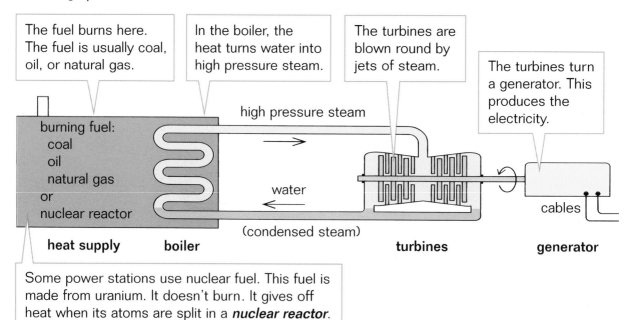

burning fuel:
coal
oil
natural gas
or
nuclear reactor

high pressure steam

water
(condensed steam)

cables

heat supply   **boiler**   **turbines**   **generator**

Some power stations use nuclear fuel. This fuel is made from uranium. It doesn't burn. It gives off heat when its atoms are split in a **nuclear reactor**.

Pollution When a power station burns fuel, its chimney gives out invisible waste gases.

Carbon dioxide adds to global warming (the greenhouse effect).

Sulphur dioxide mainly comes from coal-burning power stations. It causes acid rain.

▶ Turning the generators

In the power station on the opposite page, the generator was turned by steam.

Here are some other ways of turning generators. None of them make polluting gases:

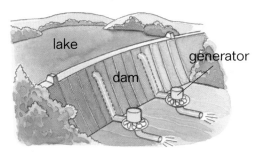

Hydroelectric power River and rainwater fill up a lake behind a dam. Water rushes down from the lake and turns the generators.

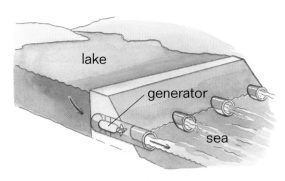

Tidal power The dam is across a river where it meets the sea. The lake fills when the tide comes in. It empties when the tide goes out. The flow of water turns the generators.

Wind power Huge windmills are blown round by the wind. There is a generator in each windmill.

1 Copy these sentences in the correct order so that they describe what happens inside a fuel-burning power station:
   The turbines turn a generator.
   The heat is used to make steam in a boiler.
   The burning fuel gives off heat.
   The generator produces electricity.
   Jets of steam blow the turbines round.

2 Five types of power station are listed on the right.
   Copy and complete these sentences. (You have to write in the types of power station which go with each one. You can choose the same type more than once.)
   The power stations that produce waste gases are....
   The power stations that do not produce waste gases are....
   The power stations that use the force of flowing water are....

> Power stations
> fuel–burning
> nuclear
> tidal
> wind
> hydroelectric

Energy supplies

▶ **Energy from the Sun**

Plants get their energy from the Sun.

Like other animals, we get our energy by eating plants - or by eating animals which have fed on plants. So all the energy for our bodies comes from the Sun.

energy

▶ **Fossil fuels**

Our main fuels are oil, natural gas, and coal. These are called *fossil fuels*. They formed from the remains of plants and tiny sea creatures that lived millions of years ago. So they store energy which once came from the Sun.

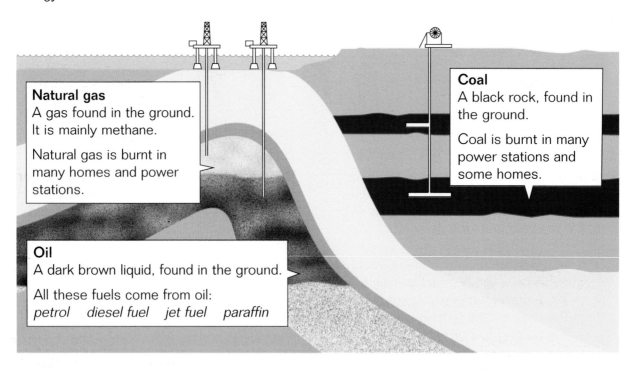

Natural gas
A gas found in the ground. It is mainly methane.

Natural gas is burnt in many homes and power stations.

Coal
A black rock, found in the ground.

Coal is burnt in many power stations and some homes.

Oil
A dark brown liquid, found in the ground.

All these fuels come from oil:
petrol   diesel fuel   jet fuel   paraffin

Our supplies of fossil fuels will not last for ever. The chart shows how many years they will last if we go on using them at the present rate.

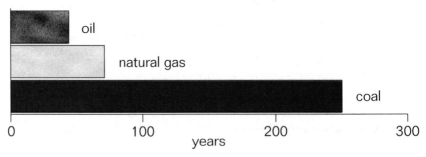

98

Biofuels

These are fuels made from plants, or from plant and animal waste.
Here are some examples:

Wood is the main fuel for many people in the world.

Alcohol can be made from sugar cane. In some countries, cars use it instead of petrol.

Methane gas comes from the rotting waste in rubbish tips and sewage works.

Renewable or non-renewable?

Some energy supplies are *renewable*. They never run out because they can always be replaced.

For example
You can grow more trees to replace those cut down.

Renewable energy supplies	Non-renewable energy supplies
Examples hydroelectric energy tidal energy wind energy biofuels	*Examples* fossil fuels: coal oil natural gas nuclear fuel

Some energy supplies are *non-renewable*. Once they have run out, they cannot be replaced.

For example
Oil can't be replaced. It takes too long to form in the ground.

1 Copy these sentences in the correct order so that they describe how the energy in our bodies came from the Sun.

Food energy is stored and used in our bodies.
Humans eat plants.
Plants take in energy from sunlight.
The Sun radiates energy.
Plants store energy in their roots and leaves.

2 Copy the table on the right.
Write *yes* or *no* in each blank space to show whether each fuel is a fossil fuel or not, and whether it is renewable or not. One example has been done for you.

Fuel	Fossil fuel?	Renewable?
wood	no	
coal		
alcohol		
oil		
natural gas		

How the world gets its energy

Solar panels
These use the Sun's rays to heat water for the house.

Solar cells
These use the energy in sunlight to produce electricity.

The Sun
Deep inside the Sun, atoms change their nuclear energy into heat. The Sun radiates more energy than a million billion billion electric fires!

Energy in food
Our bodies get energy from food. The food may be from plants, or from animals which have fed on plants.

Energy in plants
Plants take in energy from sunlight. The energy is stored in their leaves and roots as they grow.

Biofuels from plants
Biofuels are fuels from plants and other 'living' materials. Wood is a biofuel. Alcohol is a biofuel made from sugar cane.

Fossil fuels
The main fossil fuels are oil, natural gas, and coal. They formed from the remains of plants and animals that lived millions of years ago. Power stations, factories, and vehicles burn fossil fuels.

Biofuels from waste
Methane gas comes from rotting waste and sewage. It can be burnt as a fuel. Waste paper and other rubbish can also be burnt as a fuel.

Batteries
Batteries store energy. Some are given energy by charging them with electricity. Others are made from chemicals that already store energy.

Fuels from oil
Petrol, diesel fuel, jet fuel, paraffin, central heating oil, bottled gas.

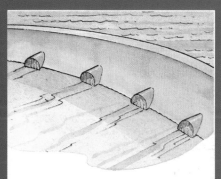

The Moon
The Moon's gravity pulls on the oceans and makes them bulge. As the Earth turns, each place has a high and low tide as it moves in and out of a bulge.

Tidal energy
As the tide comes in and goes out, the flow of water turns generators.

The atom
Some atoms have lots of nuclear energy stored in them. Changes in these atoms can release this energy.

Nuclear energy
In a nuclear reactor, uranium atoms release energy as heat. The heat is used to make steam for driving generators.

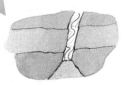

Geothermal energy
Deep underground, the rocks are very hot. The heat comes from radioactive atoms. It can be used to make steam for heating buildings or driving generators.

The weather
The Sun's heat makes winds blow across the Earth. It lifts water vapour from the oceans. Later, the water falls as rain.

Wave energy
Waves are caused by winds and tides. The up-and-down movement of the water can be used to drive generators.

Hydroelectric energy
Water rushes down from a lake and turns generators. Rainwater keeps the lake topped up.

Wind energy
For centuries, sailing ships have used the power of the wind. Today, huge windmills can turn generators.

Making sounds

► Sound waves

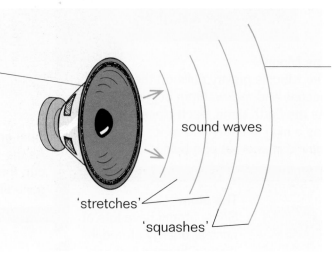

When a loudspeaker cone vibrates, it stretches and squashes the air in front.

sound waves

'stretches'

'squashes'

The 'stretches' and 'squashes' spread through the air like ripples on a pond. They are **sound waves**. In your ears, you hear them as sound.

► Features of sound

Sound needs something to move through

Sound waves can travel through gases, liquids, and solids. But they cannot travel through a vacuum (empty space).

The air has been taken out of this jar, so you cannot hear the alarm clock.

Sound is made by vibrations

Here are some things that give out sound waves when they vibrate:

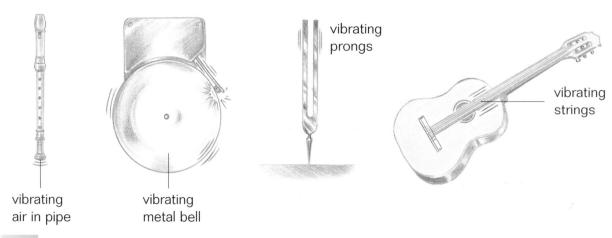

vibrating prongs

vibrating strings

vibrating air in pipe

vibrating metal bell

▶ The speed of sound

In air, the speed of sound is about 330 metres per second. This means that sound travels the length of three football pitches in a second:

The speed of light is 300 000 *kilo*metres per second. So light is much faster than sound. That is why you see a flash of lightning before you hear it.

▶ Sound on screen

If you whistle into a microphone connected to an **oscilloscope**, you see a wavy line on the screen.

oscilloscope

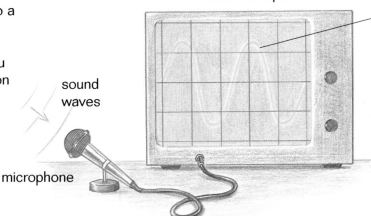

sound waves

microphone

The wavy line is a graph. It shows you how the air next to the microphone vibrates backwards and forwards as time goes on.

---

1 Here are some words connected with sound:
   oscilloscope   vacuum   air   vibrations

   Write down the word that matches each of these clues.
   a Sound can travel through this.
   b Sound cannot travel through this.
   c This instrument shows sound waves as a wavy line on a screen.
   d Sound is made by these.

2 Copy these sentences and fill in the blanks. (The information you need is somewhere on this page.)

   The speed of sound in air is.........
   The speed of light is.........
   You see a lightning flash before you hear it because.........

4.15 Hearing sounds

▶ **The ear**

This is what the ear is like inside:

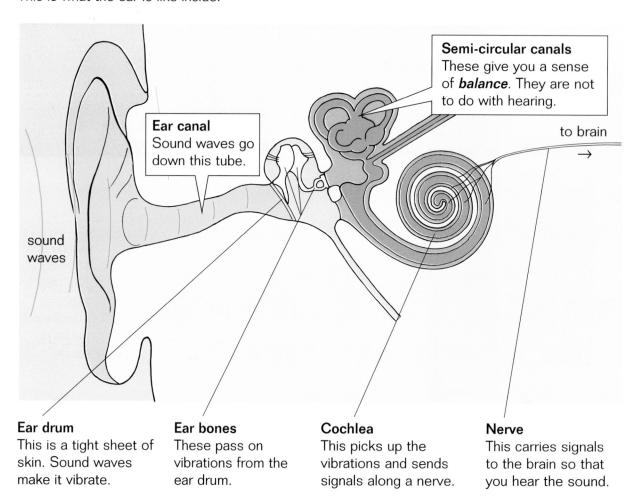

Semi-circular canals
These give you a sense of **balance**. They are not to do with hearing.

Ear canal
Sound waves go down this tube.

to brain →

sound waves

Ear drum
This is a tight sheet of skin. Sound waves make it vibrate.

Ear bones
These pass on vibrations from the ear drum.

Cochlea
This picks up the vibrations and sends signals along a nerve.

Nerve
This carries signals to the brain so that you hear the sound.

▶ **Low or high**

When you listen to a musical instrument, the note may be

low...   ...or high.

This guitar string is vibrating 200 times every second. So it is sending out 200 sound waves every second. Scientists say that the **frequency** is 200 **hertz (Hz)**.

This guitar string is vibrating faster: 400 times every second. Its frequency is 400 hertz. To the ear, the note sounds higher than before. The note has a higher **pitch**.

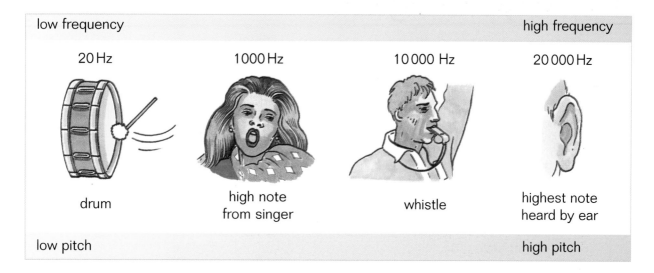

low frequency			high frequency
20 Hz	1000 Hz	10 000 Hz	20 000 Hz
drum	high note from singer	whistle	highest note heard by ear
low pitch			high pitch

▶ **Quiet or loud**

When you listen to a musical instrument, the note may be

quiet...   ...or loud.

This guitar string is making small vibrations. It is giving out a quiet sound.

This guitar string is making bigger vibrations. It is giving out a louder sound.

▶ **Hearing damage**

Very loud sounds can damage the cochlea and nerve so that the signals reaching the brain are very weak.

You should never play a personal stereo at high volume. Hours and hours of very loud music will gradually make you go deaf. But the change may be so slow that you do not notice it.

1 Copy these sentences in the correct order so that they describe how the ear works:
   The cochlea sends signals along a nerve to the brain.
   Sound waves go down the ear canal.
   The ear bones pass on the vibrations.
   Sound waves make the ear drum vibrate.
   The vibrations are picked up by the cochlea.

2 *higher   lower   louder   quieter*
   Copy these sentences. Fill in the blanks, choosing words from those above:
   If a guitar string vibrates faster, the note becomes ____.
   If the vibrations are bigger, the sound becomes ____.

4.16 Rays of light

Light is a form of energy. It is the fastest thing there is. In space and in air, it travels at a speed of........

300 000 kilometres *per second* $\longrightarrow$

▶ Reflection of light

You see things if they send light rays into your eyes.

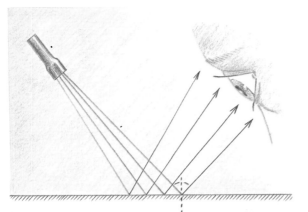

A smooth, shiny surface **reflects** light like this. Each ray strikes at an angle and bounces off at the same angle.

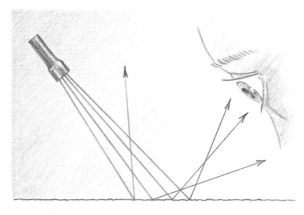

A rough surface reflects light all over the place. You see the surface because some of the light goes into your eyes.

▶ Image in a mirror

Light rays from this bulb are reflected by the mirror.

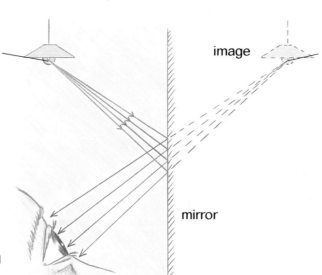

image

mirror

This person is looking towards the mirror.

The person thinks that the rays come from a place behind the mirror. So that is where she sees an *image*.

The bulb and its image are in matching positions. The image is the same distance behind the mirror as the bulb is in front.

▶ Refraction of light

A *transparent* material lets light through, so you can see through it.

Here are some transparent materials:

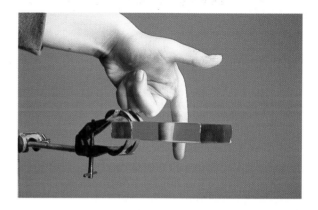

Transparent materials can bend light rays, as well as let them through.

The glass block in the photograph is bending light. The bending is called *refraction*.

This ray of light is going into a glass block. ————

When the light enters the block it bends *towards* this line. ————

When the light leaves the block, it bends *away* from this line. ————

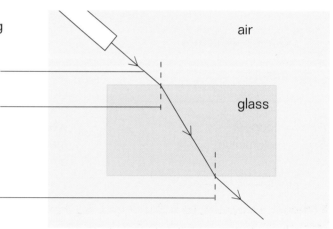

1 *refraction   transparent   reflection*

Copy these sentences. Fill in the blanks, choosing words from those above.
a If a material is _____, you can see through it.
b When light strikes a mirror, it bounces off. This is called _____.
c Light bends when it goes into a glass block. The bending is called _____.

2 Copy diagram A on the right. Draw in the rest of the ray to show where it will go after it strikes the mirror.

3 Copy diagram B on the right. Draw in the rest of the ray to show where it will go after it strikes the glass block.

4 Copy and complete this sentence:
When light shines on a piece of paper, you can see the paper because.....

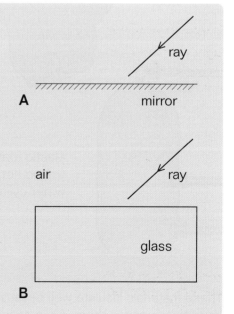

Energy on the move

Here are two ways in which energy can move:

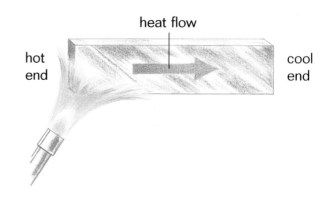

heat flow

hot end → cool end

▶ **Conduction**

If you heat one end of a metal bar, the atoms vibrate more quickly. Soon, their extra energy is passed to atoms all along the bar. Heat is moving through the bar by **conduction**. The metal is a good **conductor** of heat.

Poor conductors of heat are called **insulators**.

Good conductors	Insulators (poor conductors)	

metals
  especially
  silver
  copper
  aluminium
	glass
	water
	plastic
	wood
	materials with air trapped in them
	air
		⎡ wool
		 fibrewool
		 plastic foam
		 fur
		⎣ feathers

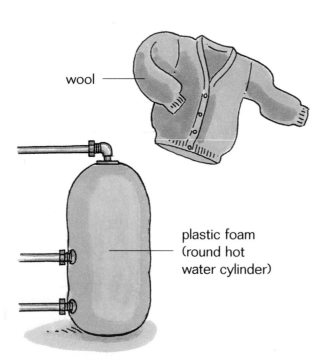

wool

plastic foam
(round hot
water cylinder)

These materials insulate well because they have air trapped in them. Air is an insulator.

Fluffed-up feathers insulate well because they trap air.

▶ Convection

When air is heated, it rises. This is because cooler, heavier air sinks and pushes it out of the way. This sets up a flow of air called a **convection current**. Other gases and liquids can also have convection currents in them.

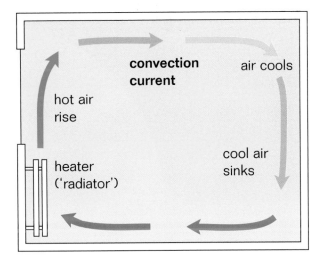

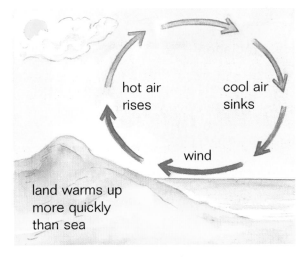

Most rooms are heated by convection. Hot air rises above a 'radiator'. This sets up a convection current which carries heat to all parts of the room.

Convection makes winds blow near the coast. During the day, the land warms up more quickly than the sea. Hot air rises above the land, as cool air blows in from the sea.

1 Copy and complete these sentences:
  Poor conductors of heat are called....
  Wool is a good insulator because....

2 *silver   glass   copper   wood
  air   plastic foam   aluminium*
  Write out the materials above in two lists, one headed 'Good conductors' and the other headed 'Insulators'.

3 Write down *two* examples of heat insulators used in clothing.

4 Write down *two* examples of heat insulators used in the home.

5 *convection   conduction   hot   cool*
  Copy the diagram on the right. Fill in the blanks, choosing words from those above.

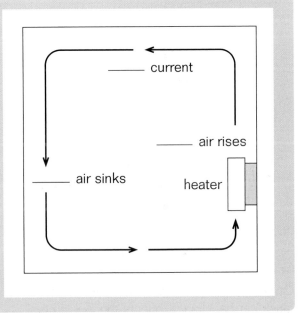

More energy on the move

This spread tells you about two more ways in which energy can move.

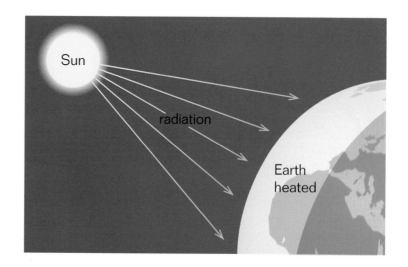

▶ **Heat radiation**

On Earth, we are warmed by the Sun. The rays that warm us are called **heat radiation** (thermal radiation). They travel to Earth through empty space.

All hot things give off heat radiation. But some surfaces are better at giving it off than others.	**Giving off radiation**

best ·························· worst

| dull black | shiny black | white | shiny and light |

When heat radiation strikes something, it may be *reflected* (bounced off) or *absorbed* (taken in).	**Reflecting radiation**
	Absorbing radiation

Reflecting radiation: worst ·················· best

Absorbing radiation: best ·················· worst

On a sunny day, a white car is cooler than a black car because it reflects the Sun's rays.

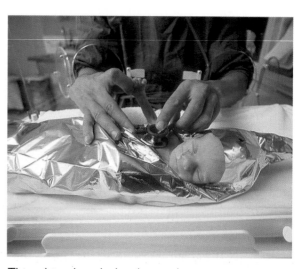

This shiny bag helps keep the premature baby warm.

Vacuum flask This can keep a drink hot for hours. The heat escapes very slowly:

Shiny surfaces cut down the heat lost by *radiation*.

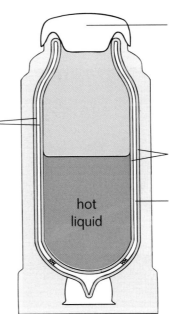

The stopper stops heat being lost by *convection*.

glass or steel

A part-vacuum (space with air missing) cuts down the heat lost by *conduction*.

hot liquid

▶ Evaporation

Wet hands dry out in a few minutes. This is because the water *evaporates* (changes into vapour). If air is blowing from a drier, the water evaporates much faster.

As your hands dry, they feel colder. This is because heat is needed to turn water into vapour (see Spread 3.02). The vapour takes the heat from your hands, so they cool down.

INITIAL

1 Copy and complete these sentences by writing MORE or LESS in each blank space.
  a A white kettle loses heat _____ quickly than a black kettle.
  b A white car reflects _____ of the Sun's rays than a black car.
  c A white car absorbs _____ of the Sun's rays than a black car.
  d If air blows over wet hands, the water evaporates _____ quickly.

2 Choose the word on the right that which goes with each of these. (You can use the same word more than once.)
  a Heat reaches us from the Sun like this.
  b A flask is shiny so that less heat is lost like this.
  c A flask needs a stopper to stop heat being lost like this.

conduction

convection

radiation

Seeing colours

▶ **A spectrum**

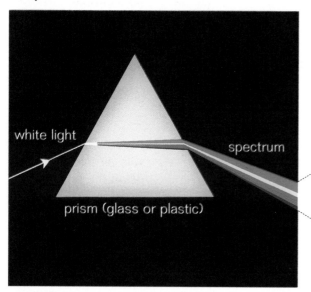

White light is not a single colour, but a mixture of colours. A **_prism_** splits them up.

The light is refracted (bent) when it goes into the prism, and when it comes out.

The refracted light spreads to form a range of colours called a **_spectrum_**:

red
orange
yellow
green
blue
violet

The spreading effect is called **_dispersion_**.

▶ **Making white**

The human eye doesn't need all the colours in the spectrum to see white. Red, green, and blue are enough. If beams of red, green, and blue light overlap on a white screen, they make white.

Red, green, and blue are called the **_primary colours_**.

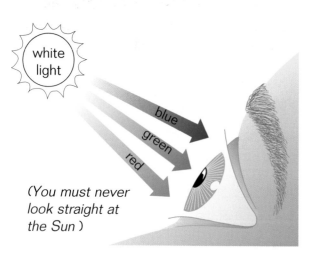

(You must never look straight at the Sun)

The Sun glows and gives out white light. So does a bulb. To the eye, the white light is the same as a mixture of red, green, and blue.

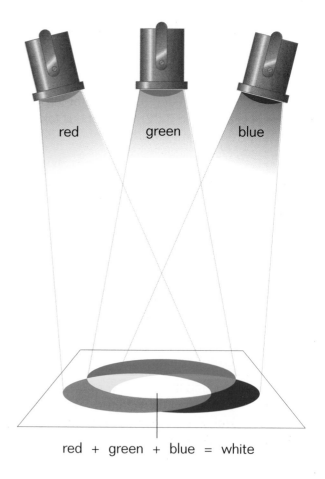

red + green + blue = white

▶ Why things look coloured

Most things don't glow. We see them because they reflect light from the Sun or a lamp. However, only some colours may be reflected. The rest are *absorbed* (taken away).

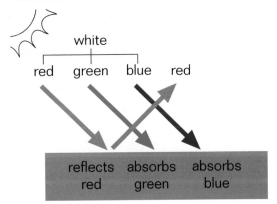

This patch reflects only red light. So it looks red. It absorbs green and blue.

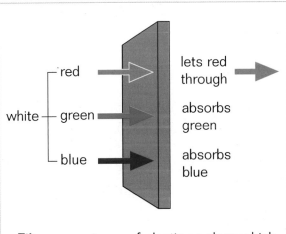

Filters are pieces of plastic or glass which only let some colours through. For example, a red filter lets red light through, but absorbs green and blue.

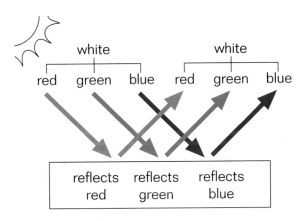

This patch reflects red, green, and blue, so it looks white. It absorbs no colours.

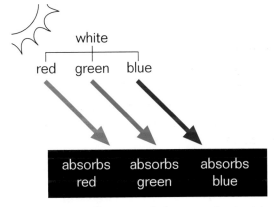

This patch reflects no light, so it looks black. It absorbs red, green, and blue.

1 Copy and complete these sentences:
   A triangular glass block is called......
   It can split white light into a range of colours called......

2 On the right, there is a list of colours. Write down the colour or colours which go with each of these statements. (You can choose the same colours more than once.)
   a When white light goes through a prism, this colour is refracted (bent) the least.
   b If these colours overlap on a white screen, they make white.
   c A red filter lets this colour through.
   d If something absorbs all the light striking it, it looks this colour.
   e A red book absorbs these colours.

white

black

red

green

blue

Sun and Earth

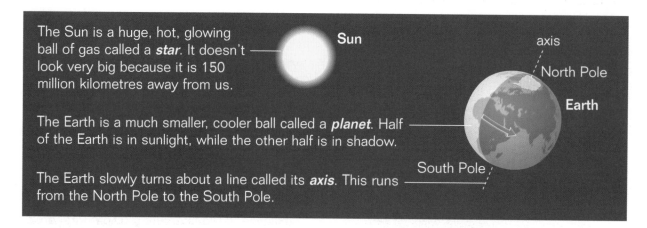

The Sun is a huge, hot, glowing ball of gas called a *star*. It doesn't look very big because it is 150 million kilometres away from us.

Sun

axis

North Pole

Earth

The Earth is a much smaller, cooler ball called a *planet*. Half of the Earth is in sunlight, while the other half is in shadow.

South Pole

The Earth slowly turns about a line called its *axis*. This runs from the North Pole to the South Pole.

▶ Day and night

The Earth takes **one day** (24 hours) to turn once on its axis. As it turns, places move from the sunlit half into the shadow half. So they move from daytime into night.

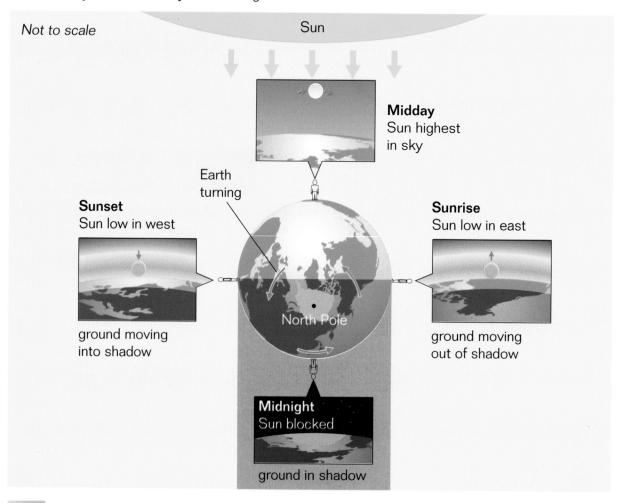

Not to scale

Sun

Midday
Sun highest in sky

Earth turning

Sunset
Sun low in west

ground moving into shadow

North Pole

Sunrise
Sun low in east

ground moving out of shadow

Midnight
Sun blocked

ground in shadow

The year and seasons

The Earth moves around the Sun in a big circle called an **orbit**.
The Earth takes **one year** (about 365 days) to orbit the Sun.

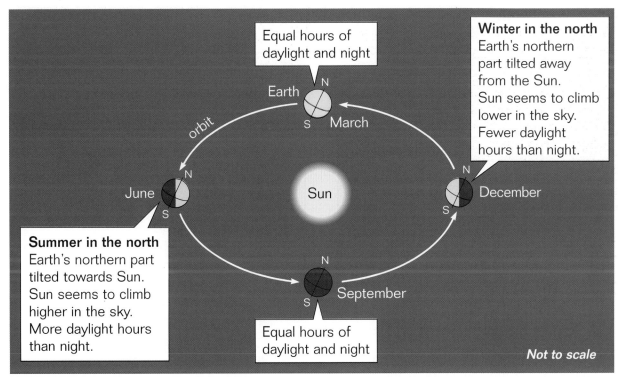

Equal hours of daylight and night

Earth

March

Winter in the north
Earth's northern part tilted away from the Sun.
Sun seems to climb lower in the sky.
Fewer daylight hours than night.

orbit

June

Sun

December

Summer in the north
Earth's northern part tilted towards Sun.
Sun seems to climb higher in the sky.
More daylight hours than night.

September

Equal hours of daylight and night

Not to scale

The Earth's axis leans by about 23°. This means that the Earth's northern part is sometimes tilted towards the Sun and sometimes away from it.

In June, the Earth's northern part is tilted towards the Sun. That is when the Sun seems to climb highest in the sky and there are most hours of daylight. So it is summer.

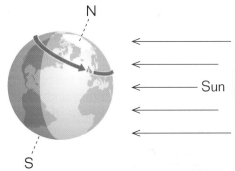

Sun

1 *24 hours   7 days   365 days*
Copy these sentences. Fill in the blanks, choosing times from those above. (You can use the same time more than once.)

There are ____ in one day.
There are about ____ in one year.
The Earth takes about ____ to orbit the Sun.
The Earth takes ____ to turn once on its axis.

2 a Copy the diagram on the right. Shade in the part of the Earth that is in shadow.
 b Write down whether it is *daytime* or *night* in Britain.
 c Write down whether it is *summer* or *winter* in Britain.

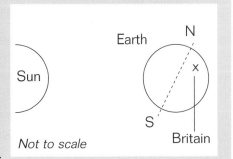

Sun

Earth

Britain

Not to scale

Orbiting the Earth

▶ Satellites in orbit

There are hundreds of satellites in orbit around the Earth.
Here are some of the jobs they do:

Communications satellites These pass on TV and telephone signals.

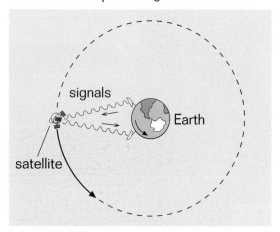

This satellite is in a *geostationary* orbit. It goes round at the same rate as the Earth turns. So it always seems to stay in the same place in the sky.

Weather satellites These send pictures down to Earth so that forecasters can see what the weather is doing.

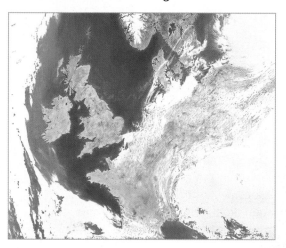

This satellite picture shows the weather over Europe.

Research satellites Some of these carry telescopes for looking at stars and planets. Above the atmosphere, they get a much clearer view.

This is the Hubble Space Telescope. It radios its pictures back to Earth.

Navigation satellites These send out signals so that a ship or aircraft can work out its position.

This GPS receiver picks up signals from satellites, calculates its position, and shows the result.

The Moon

The Moon orbits the Earth. It is smaller than the Earth, and has a rocky surface with lots of craters.

The Moon is *not* hot and glowing like the Sun.

We can only see the Moon because its surface reflects sunlight. We don't see the part that is in shadow.

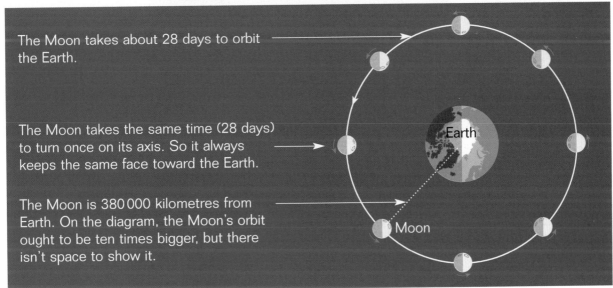

The Moon takes about 28 days to orbit the Earth.

The Moon takes the same time (28 days) to turn once on its axis. So it always keeps the same face toward the Earth.

The Moon is 380 000 kilometres from Earth. On the diagram, the Moon's orbit ought to be ten times bigger, but there isn't space to show it.

Earth

Moon

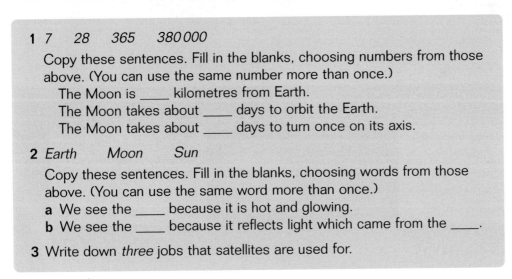

1 *7   28   365   380 000*

Copy these sentences. Fill in the blanks, choosing numbers from those above. (You can use the same number more than once.)

The Moon is _____ kilometres from Earth.

The Moon takes about _____ days to orbit the Earth.

The Moon takes about _____ days to turn once on its axis.

2 *Earth   Moon   Sun*

Copy these sentences. Fill in the blanks, choosing words from those above. (You can use the same word more than once.)

a We see the _____ because it is hot and glowing.

b We see the _____ because it reflects light which came from the _____.

3 Write down *three* jobs that satellites are used for.

The Solar System

The Sun has lots of **planets** orbiting it. The Sun and its planets are called the **Solar System**.

This diagram shows how the sizes of the Sun and planets compare (the distances are not correct):

The inner planets These are mainly made of rock.

The asteroids These are thousands of tiny planets. The largest is only 1000 km across.

The outer planets Apart from Pluto, these are large and mainly made of gas. Saturn's rings are billions of bits of ice.

Planet ▶	Mercury	Venus	Earth	Mars	Jupiter	Saturn	Uranus	Neptune	Pluto
Distance from the Sun in million km	58	108	150	228	778	1430	2870	4500	5900
Time for one orbit (y=year, d=day)	88 d	225 d	1 y	1.9 y	12 y	29 y	84 y	165 y	247 y
Diameter in km	4900	12100	12800	6800	143000	120000	51000	49000	3900
Average surface temperature	350 °C	480 °C	22 °C	−23 °C	−150 °C	−180 °C	−210 °C	−220 °C	−230 °C
Number of moons	0	0	1	2	16	23	15	8	1

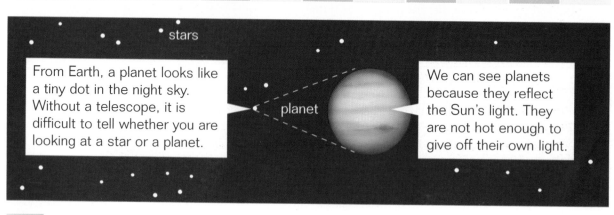

stars

From Earth, a planet looks like a tiny dot in the night sky. Without a telescope, it is difficult to tell whether you are looking at a star or a planet.

planet

We can see planets because they reflect the Sun's light. They are not hot enough to give off their own light.

▶ Orbits

This diagram shows how the sizes of the planets' orbits compare:

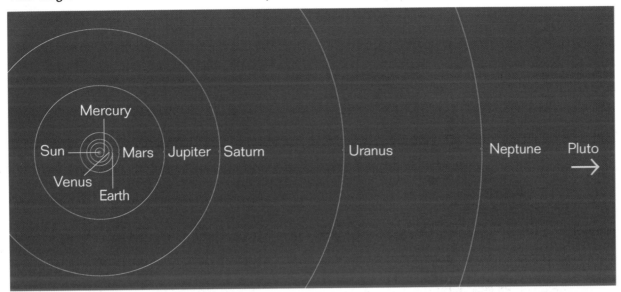

▶ Gravity in action

Gravity is a force.

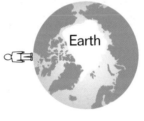

The Earth's gravity holds us on the ground.

Earth

The Earth's gravity holds the Moon in its orbit around the Earth.

The Sun's gravity holds the Earth and other planets in their orbits around the Sun.

There is a pull of gravity between *all* masses. But to produce a strong pull, one mass has to be very large – like the Earth.

1 Copy and complete each of these sentences by writing in the name of a planet:
   The biggest planet is.....
   The planet nearest the Sun is.....
   The hottest planet is.....
   The planet furthest from the Sun is.....
   The coldest planet is.....
   The planet with most moons is.....
   The planet which takes the least time to orbit the Sun is.....
   The planet which takes the most time to orbit the Sun is.....

2 Write down the name of the force which holds the planets in their orbits around the Sun.

Test questions

Test total: 20 marks

1 The sparrowhawk (below) feeds on other birds.

a) Give *two* features of the sparrowhawk which help it catch and eat its prey. [2]

b) Give *one* feature which helps it cope with cold conditions. [1]

2 Harry is working in the kitchen with his sister, Louise. Harry has a cold. Write down *three* ways in which Harry's germs might spread to Louise. [3]

3 The diagram below shows inside a human arm.

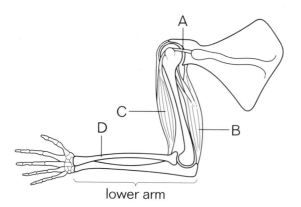

Four parts, A, B, C, and D, have been labelled.

a) Give one part which is made of bone. [1]

b) Give one part which is a muscle. [1]

c) Which part must contract (get shorter) for the lower arm to be raised? [1]

4 The diagram below shows the inside of the lungs. The lungs are filled with air, which is mainly a mixture of nitrogen, oxygen, water vapour, and carbon dioxide.

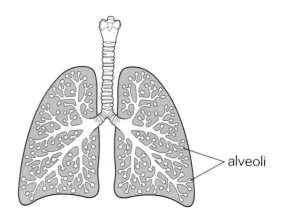

alveoli

a) Give *three* ways in which the air you breathe out is different from the air you breathe in. [3]

b) Explain why the alveoli are surrounded by lots of tiny blood vessels (tubes). [1]

c) Explain why, when you are exercising, you have to breathe faster. [2]

5

Vicky has a tree in her garden and some grass. The grass is much thicker and longer in the open areas than near the tree.

a) The tree has a large root system. Give *two* things which the tree must take in through its roots in order to grow properly. [2]

b) Give *two* reasons why the grass does not grow so well near the tree. [2]

c) Give an example of how another form of wildlife (apart from grass) might be affected if the tree was cut down. [1]

Test questions

Test total: 20 marks

1

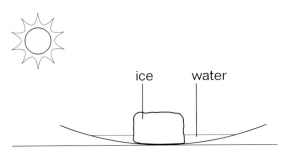

ice   water

a) In the diagram above, an ice cube has been left in a saucer out in the sunshine on a warm, dry day. Is each of the following happening?
   i) A solid is changing into a liquid (YES/NO) [1]
   ii) A liquid is changing into a gas. (YES/NO) [1]

b) *evaporating   freezing   melting   condensing*
   Which of the above words describes each of the following?
   i) A solid changing into a liquid
   ii) A liquid changing into a gas
   iii) A gas changing into a liquid.   [3]

2

The beaker above contains a mixture of salt and sand. Describe how you would separate the salt from the sand.   [3]

3 Physical changes in materials are easy to reverse, chemical changes are not. Write down whether each of the following is an example of a *physical change* or a *chemical change*.
   a) Boiling water changing into steam
   b) A raw egg cooking and becoming hard-boiled
   c) Wet cement drying and setting hard.   [3]

4 Adam used indicator paper to measure the pH of four liquids. Here are his results:

	pH
vinegar:	3
oven cleaner:	13
liquid soap:	8
kitchen cleaner:	11

a) Which liquid is the most acidic?   [1]
b) Which liquid is the most alkaline?   [1]
c) Which liquid would turn blue litmus paper red?   [1]
d) Wasp stings are alkaline. Which liquid would you use to neutralize a wasp sting?   [1]
e) If Adam measured the pH of pure water, what result would he get?   [1]

5 Here are descriptions of four different rocks:
   A Granite. This is made up of tiny crystals, formed when hot magma cooled.
   B Basalt. This is made up of tiny crystals, but much smaller than those in granite.
   C Limestone. This sometimes contains fossils.
   D Marble. This is formed when limestone gets heated in the ground.

a) Decide whether each of the rocks A to D is *igneous*, *sedimentary*, or *metamorphic*.   [4]
b) The granite tor below has cracked and pieces have broken off. Why has this happened?   [2]

Test questions

Test total: 20 marks

1

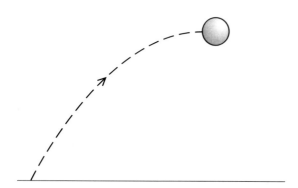

The diagram above shows a football travelling through the air after it has been kicked.
a) What is the name of the force that is slowing the football down? Copy the diagram and draw in an arrow to show this force. [2]
b) What other force is acting on the ball? Use an arrow to show this on your diagram. [2]

2 Matthew saw a flash of lightning. One second later he heard the crash of sound.
a) Why did Matthew hear the crash after he saw the flash? [1]
a) When Matthew saw another flash, there was a two-second delay before he heard the sound. What did this tell him about the lightning? [1]

3 Latha is carrying out tests with magnets and other materials to find out what magnetic forces there are between them. For each of the tests below, write down whether there is a force of *attraction*, or *repulsion*, or *no force*. [3]

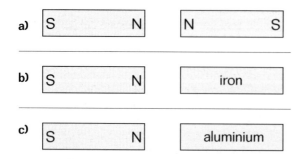

4

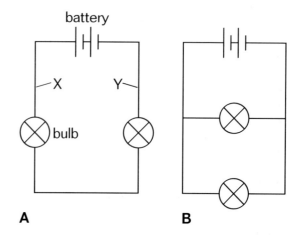

A   **B**

Lauren wants to connect two bulbs to a battery. She tries two different circuits, A and B above.
a) When Lauren connects an ammeter into circuit A at point X, it read 0.1 A. If she puts the ammeter at Y instead, will its reading be *more*, *less*, or the *same* as before? [1]
b) Lauren finds that the bulbs in one of the circuits are brighter than in the other. In which circuit are the bulbs brighter? [1]
c) If one bulb is removed from each circuit, leaving a gap in the wire, how is the other bulb affected i) in circuit A ii) in circuit B? [2]

5 This table shows some of our energy resources:

Energy resource	Renewable resource?	Energy originally from the Sun?
oil		YES
hydroelectric		
wind		
nuclear		
wood		
solar (cells)		

a) What is meant by a *renewable* resource? [1]
b) The energy stored in oil originally came from the Sun. Explain how the energy got from the Sun into the oil. [2]
c) Copy the table and complete it by writing YES or NO in each blank space. [4]

Answers

2.01

1 plants; cells; body
2 a) nucleus b) chloroplast c) tissue
3 Labels, from top: nucleus, animal, cell wall, plant.
4 Cell wall, chloroplasts

2.02

1 Leaves shaded in
2 sunlight; carbon dioxide, oxygen; oxygen, carbon dioxide; oxygen
3 Water goes in through roots, then moves up water tubes
4 Minerals go in through roots with water
5 Gases pass in and out through tiny holes

2.03

1 pollen (top left), nectar (bottom left), ovules (top right), petal (bottom right)
2 female; male; pollination
3 a) To attract insects b) Looking for nectar c) Pollen sticks to bee's body, bee flies to another flower, pollen sticks to this flower

2.04

1 fertilization; germination
2 Sentence order is 5th, 2nd, 6th, 3rd, 1st, 4th
3 Water, warmth, air
4 Seed falls slowly and is blown by wind

2.05

1 a) stomach b) lung c) heart d) kidney
2 Brain (in head); lung (in chest)
3 Food, water, oxygen
4 From kidneys (through bladder), from lungs

2.06

1 skull; ribs; backbone
2 a) teeth b) muscles c) nerves
3 calcium; ligaments; tendons

2.07

1 blood; digestion; enzymes
2 Sentence order is 3rd, 6th, 1st, 5th, 2nd, 4th

2.08

1 a) petrol, oxygen b) food, oxygen c) carbon dioxide, water d) carbon dioxide, water

2 a) artery b) vein c) capillary
3 To bring in food and oxygen (for respiration), and take away carbon dioxide and water

2.09

1 From top: windpipe, lung, heart, rib, diaphragm
2 ribs, diaphragm, lungs, blood
3 Oxygen
4 carbon dioxide
5 To keep replacing air in lungs so that oxygen and carbon dioxide can be exchanged

2.10

1 Sentence order is 3rd, 2nd, 1st
2 a) testicles b) ovaries c) fertilization

2.11

1 a) bag of watery liquid b) umbilical cord c) placenta
2 Sentence order is 5th, 4th, 1st, 6th, 3rd, 2nd
3 Baby's blood gets food and oxygen from mother's blood, in the placenta

2.12

1 carbohydrates, fats; proteins
2 Ticks to show the following: carbohydrate in bread; fat in cheese; protein in bread, milk, and cheese
3 Cheese, milk
4 Vegetables, bread
5 Blackcurrants, oranges
6 a) ...it is used in making bones and teeth b) ...it helps food pass through gut more easily

2.13

1 a) germs b) infection c) immune d) antibodies e) vaccine
2 From sneeze, from dirty food, from dirty hands touching food
3 So that germs on hands won't get on food

2.14

1 Sentences:
 1st on left goes with 4th on right;
 2nd on left goes with 5th on right;
 3rd on left goes with 6th on right;
 4th on left goes with 3rd on right;
 5th on left goes with 1st on right;
 6th on left goes with 2nd on right

2 So that they won't catch German measles during first three months of pregnancy, as this would harm baby

2.15
1 a) Four legs, one tail, two ears b) Length of legs, length of tail, colour of fur
2 Height, length of hair, colour of ears
3 Size of muscles
4 Breeding race horses for speed

2.16
1 Ticks to show the following:
all have backbones; all have lungs;
fish, amphibians, and reptiles have scales; birds have feathers; mammals have fur;
fish, amphibians, reptiles, and birds lay eggs; mammals have babies; birds and mammals have a steady body temperature; also H is at top of 'Mammals' column.

2.17
1 a) frog b) polar bear c) human
2 Cutting down trees, digging up soil
3 a) ...it stops it getting light and water
  b) ...it may eat it

2.18
1 a) Large eyes b) Large claws
  c) Sharp beak d) Feathers which can trap air
2 Difficult for it to be seen by animals that might eat it
3 Sentences: 1st on left goes with 4th on right; 2nd on left goes with 3rd on right; 3rd on left goes with 5th on right; 4th on left goes with 1st on right; 5th on left goes with 2nd on right

2.19
1 cabbage → caterpillar → thrush → fox
2 ...the cabbage; ...the caterpillar, thrush, and fox
3 octopus, crab, seal, seagull

3.01
1 Ticks and crosses to show the following: solid has fixed shape, fixed volume, and can't flow; liquid has fixed shape, no fixed volume, and can flow; gas has no fixed shape, no fixed volume, and can flow
2 a) petrol b) lead, gold c) air d) water
3 a) 1000 b) 2

3.02
1 liquid; gas; solid; liquid
2 a) mercury, water b) aluminium, iron

3.03
1 a) gas b) solid c) liquid
2 ...gas particles from the perfume are pushed around by gas particles in the air. (Diffusion) ...gas particles in the balloon keep hitting the sides and pushing on them.

3.04
1 metals; atoms; metals; nonmetals; compounds
2 hydrogen, oxygen, carbon, nitrogen, sulphur
3 Table: water is made from hydrogen and oxygen; carbon dioxide is made from carbon and oxygen; sulphuric acid is made from hydrogen, oxygen, and sulphur

3.05
1 a) pure substance b) alloy
2 dissolves; soluble; solvent; solution

3.06
1 a) dissolving and filtering b) dissolving and filtering c) filtering, or distilling
  d) chromatography
2 Tea-leaves, liquid tea (mainly water)
3 Dust, air

3.07
1 From top: (acid), acid, alkali, acid, alkali, acid, acid
2 a) dilute b) concentrated c) hydrogen d) ...it has cancelled out the acid effect e) ...7

3.08
1 a) chemical b) chemical c) physical
2 From top: chemical, physical, physical, chemical, chemical, physical, chemical

3.09
1 a) carbon dioxide b) oxygen c) carbon dioxide d) methane e) oxygen f) carbon dioxide g) carbon dioxide
2 air (oxygen), heat, fuel

3.10
1 Air, water
2 Coating with paint, coating with grease
3 a) oxide b) hydrogen
4 a) magnesium b) magnesium c) gold

3.11
1 a) nitrogen b) oxygen c) carbon dioxide
   d) nitrogen
2 a) Helium, ...it is lighter than other gases in air
   b) Carbon dioxide, ...things can't burn in it
   c) Nitrogen, ...it doesn't make food go off
3 Neon, used in some lamps

3.12
1 a) Sodium chloride b) Carbon dioxide
2 a) NO b) YES c) YES
3 ...water vapour condenses on cold ground or
   plants; ...frost; ...water expands when it freezes

3.13
1 a) erosion b) sediment c) humus
2 Sentence order is 4th, 5th, 3rd, 1st, 2nd

3.14
1 a) sedimentary b) igneous c) metamorphic
2 granite (igneous) used for chippings; limestone
   (sedimentary) used in cement; slate
   (metamorphic) used in snooker tables

4.01
1 a) current b) insulator
2 Ticks to show the following: copper, aluminium,
   and carbon are good conductors; water and air
   are poor conductors; plastic and glass are
   insulators
3 a) Torch, TV remote controller, mobile phone
   b) Toaster, table lamp (or any mains appliances)
   c) Solar-powered calculator

4.02
1 ammeter; current; current
2 ...a voltmeter; ...an ammeter; ...2.0

4.03
1 a) B b) Because the voltage across it is higher,
   so the current through it is higher
2 a) C b) D c) It will go out d) It will stay bright

4.04
1 south; north; north
2 Ticks to show the following: nickel, iron, and
   steel are magnetic; aluminium and copper are
   non-magnetic
3 a) Steel b) Iron c) Iron

4.05
1 weight; friction; tension; air resistance
2 newton

3 Force of 6 N downwards from centre of ball

4.06
1 a) low b) high c) high d) low
2 newtons per square metre
3 a) 2 b) $2 N/m^2$

4.07
1 A, ...it is longer
2 ...she is lighter than person A
3 Y, ...its centre of gravity is not over the table
   underneath, so its weight has a turning effect
   which will pull it over

4.08
1 speed; 20; 40
2 From top: useful, useful, problem, useful,
   problem, useful
3 Streamlined helmet, streamlined frame,
   streamlined wheels, crouching position

4.09
1 joules; forms
2 Examples, from top: torch beam, moving car,
   petrol, stretched spring

4.10
1 TRUE; FALSE
2 hot water bottle; plant; hairdrier; candle

4.11
1 Sentence order is 3rd, 2nd, 5th, 1st, 4th
2 fuel-burning; nuclear, tidal, wind, and
   hydroelectric; tidal and hydroelectric

4.12
1 Sentence order is 4th, 3rd, 5th, 2nd, 1st
2 'yes' and 'no' to show the following:
   coal, oil, and natural gas are fossil fuels; wood
   and alcohol are renewable

4.14
1 a) air b) vacuum c) oscilloscope
   d) vibrations
2 ...about 330 metres per second;
   ...300 000 kilometres per second;
   ...the light travels much faster than the sound

4.15
1 Sentence order is 2nd, 4th, 3rd, 5th,1st
2 higher; louder

4.16

1 a) transparent b) reflection c) refraction
2 Ray should reflect from mirror at same angle as it arrives
3 Ray should bend downwards slightly as it goes into glass (as in diagram on p107); ray should bend again as it leaves glass, so that its direction is parallel to the direction it first had
4 ...it reflects light into your eyes

4.17

1 ...insulators; ...it traps air
2 Good conductors: silver, copper, aluminium. Insulators: glass, wood, air, plastic foam
3 Wool in gloves, fibre filling in coats
4 Plastic foam round hot water tanks, plastic handles on saucepans
5 Labels: convection (top), cool (left), hot (right)

4.18

1 a) LESS b) MORE c) LESS d) MORE
2 a) radiation b) radiation c) convection

4.19

1 ...a prism; ...a spectrum
2 a) red b) red, green, and blue c) red d) black e) green and blue

4.20

1 24 hours; 365 days; 365 days; 24 hours
2 a) Right half of Earth should be in shadow (edge of shadow should be vertical) b) night c) winter

4.21

1 380 000; 28; 28
2 a) Sun b) Moon, Sun
3 Communications, navigation, watching the weather

4.22

1 Jupiter; Mercury; Mercury; Pluto; Pluto; Saturn; Mercury; Pluto
2 Gravity

Test questions (Section 2)

1 a) Sharp beak, large claws b) Feathers which can trap air
2 Sneezing into air, onto food, contact with saliva
3 a) D b) B or C c) C
4 a) Less oxygen, more carbon dioxide, more water vapour b) So that gases can pass in/out of blood c) Take in oxygen faster, get rid of carbon dioxide faster
5 a) Water, minerals b) Less light, water and minerals taken by tree c) Birds lose nesting places

Test questions (Section 3)

1 a) i) YES ii) YES b) i) melting ii) evaporating iii) condensing
2 Add water to dissolve salt, filter mixture to remove sand
3 a) physical change b) chemical change c) chemical change
4 a) vinegar b) oven cleaner c) vinegar d) vinegar e) 7
5 a) A and B igneous, C sedimentary, D metamorphic b) Heating/cooling has caused cracks, water has frozen and expanded in cracks

Test questions (Section 4)

1 a) Air resistance (or friction), horizontal arrow from ball pointing to left b) Gravity, downward arrow from ball
2 a) Sound slower than light b) Further away (twice as far)
3 a) repulsion b) attraction c) no force
4 a) same b) B c) i) Goes off ii) Stays on
5 a) Can be replaced when used up b) Ancient sea plants absorbed Sun's energy, ancient sea creatures fed on plants, remains of plants and creatures trapped and crushed by sediment to form oil c) Table to show the following: all except oil and nuclear are renewable; all except nuclear got energy from Sun

Index

*The main topics are in **bold**.*